MARGIN + MISSION

A Prescription for Curing Healthcare's Cost Crisis

SECOND EDITION

Dan Michelson & Liz Kirk

Strata Decision Technology

Strata Decision Technology
200 E. Randolph, Chicago, IL 60601
marginmission@stratadecision.com
www.stratadecision.com
Copyright© 2018
All rights reserved.
Second Edition, January 2018
Circulation of 2500 copies

Contents

Introduction

Margin + Mission: A Prescription for

Curing Healthcare's Cost Crisis

By Dan Michelson

Sister Irene Kraus was the founding chief executive of the Daughters of Charity National Health System, one of the largest non-profit hospital chains in the country. And she was the only woman to chair the American Hospital Association.

Impressive.

But what she may be most remembered for is coining the phrase, "No Margin, No Mission" – a mantra that is a roadmap for healthcare and the inspiration for this book.

Sister Irene believed that strong fiscal management, not just charity, is what hospitals needed to fulfill their mission. "In the United States in this day and age," she would say, "the way to do it is to run institutions that are financially solid." That is, in order to fulfill your mission, you must drive margin.

Never have the words of Sister Irene been more important than right now. The healthcare industry is on the threshold of taking on what might well be its biggest challenge ever – financial stewardship. The topic is now front and center, not only within the industry, but on the national political and media stage as well. Wherever you turn, you hear about the runaway train of healthcare cost. On a per capita basis, the U.S. will spend twice as much as any other industrialized nation. In 2018 the healthcare bill will be well over $3 trillion, about 18 percent of our gross domestic product.

To put that in perspective, that's over four times the amount we will spend on national defense, which is pretty ironic as the structure of our current business model in healthcare started with a war.

During World War II, the federal government imposed wage and price controls to limit inflation and address a labor shortage. As a trade-off, new benefits were introduced, including allowing employer-based health insurance to be excluded from taxable income. In response, the number of Americans with private health insurance exploded from 20 million at the beginning of the 1940s to over 140 million by decade's end. By 1965, the introduction of Medicare and Medicaid would add another 40 million Americans into a system that compensated healthcare providers based on volume – the more they did, the more they would make.

An entire industry – consultants, competencies, companies – arose to help healthcare providers take advantage of the new payment system by maximizing their revenue. With zero incentive for managing costs or increasing efficiency, the gains that transformed most businesses in the 1970s and 1980s bypassed healthcare altogether. American healthcare costs spiraled out of control. More equaled more.

It's no surprise then that 50 years later American healthcare is on life support. Hospitals, which have been the structural hub for healthcare, have seen their operating margins plummet to close to 2 percent. One in three hospitals carries negative operating margins, according to Standard & Poor's. Banking margins, by comparison, average 27 percent.

Without a big shift in approach, the future for hospitals and health systems is cloudy at best as they are facing a perfect storm – an unprecedented mix of challenges that endangers their financial viability. Patient volumes are decreasing as the focus continues to shift to keeping patients out of hospitals, the most expensive care setting. Reimbursement from Medicare, which covers a majority of hospital services, is decreasing for the first time in decades. Competition and market consolidation are on the rise as more independent hospitals seek refuge within larger, well-funded regional health systems.

Meanwhile, insurance companies are increasingly switching to a capitated model that pays healthcare providers a set fee for each enrolled person, meaning providers can no longer rely on getting paid for every service they deliver. The effect of all of these changes is that hospitals' decades-old strategy of growing top line revenue is quickly becoming outdated. Reducing the total cost of care has become the number one strategic concern for healthcare providers, according to a survey by the *Healthcare Information Management Systems Society*. Many hospitals and healthcare delivery systems today have set annual cost takeout targets of over $100 million.

That amount of belt tightening for an industry that represents close to one-fifth of our GDP requires a massive change in mindset and skillset. Unfortunately, after 50 years of focusing only on generating revenue, most hospitals lack the skills and staff for the transition. Results from a survey of 100 hospital finance executives show that while nearly nine of 10 have a cost reduction target, seven of 10 felt their efforts were falling flat.

Why? For the vast majority of hospitals, cost information is a black hole. They simply don't have it. The article in the *Harvard Business Review*, 'The Strategy That Will Fix Healthcare,' spelled out this problem in no uncertain terms: "For a field in which high cost is an overarching problem, the absence of accurate cost information in healthcare is nothing short of astounding," wrote authors Michael Porter and Thomas Lee. "Without understanding the true costs of care for patient conditions, much less how costs are related to outcomes, healthcare organizations are flying blind in deciding how to improve processes and redesign care."

At the same time, with one in five individuals in employer-sponsored plans now opting for high deductible health plans, consumer interest in the price of healthcare is at a fever pitch. Thirty-five states now require hospitals to make public what they charge for procedures and tests. While this sounds reasonable to those outside of healthcare, to those who work inside it represents an enormous problem. How can providers make their prices public when they don't know their costs?

By analyzing cost and margins as a baseline, administrators can begin to share data with clinicians and engage them in a process of continuous improvement: using algorithms instead of anecdotes to understand the cost of variation, waste, harm and other factors that drive cost up and then working together to drive cost out.

What is emerging is one of the great socioeconomic opportunities of our time – helping healthcare shift away from a revenue cycle model of maximizing the top line to an approach of managing the bottom line from a clinical and financial perspective.

The goal of this book – *Margin + Mission: A Prescription for Curing Healthcare's Cost Crisis* – is to share ideas on how we can solve the cost crisis in healthcare and to drive margin to fuel mission.

Hospitals and healthcare systems are the hub for healthcare, both physically and fiscally, representing close to $1 trillion of the total cost. This book focuses on the issue of cost and what can be done about it within that segment because of their ability to directly reduce cost in their own organizations, as well as their potential to influence the level of spend in the market.

In Part One we identify the problem and drill into the root causes. In Part Two, we offer solutions and the emergence of cost accounting as a "killer app". In Part Three, we highlight best practices in bending the cost curve from some of healthcare most prominent organizations. Lastly, in Part Four, we outline how you can develop your roadmap to drive and deliver value.

This book is a curation and compilation of articles from a number of publications and ideas from key stakeholders that together we believe will help advance the dialogue on this critical topic at this critical time.

Our hope is our second edition of *Margin + Mission, A Prescription for Curing Healthcare's Cost Crisis*, provides inspiration, fuels conversation and drives action to make a meaningful difference in bending the cost curve. It won't be easy. Curing healthcare's cost crisis will require as much investment and energy devoted to delivering value in the next 50 years as has been spent driving volume over the past 50 years. But in the new world of healthcare, where driving margin can only be achieved by delivering high quality care and improving patient health, we will all benefit.

As Sister Irene outlined long ago, for healthcare to be healthy, margin plus mission must be the prescription.

PART ONE

Understanding the Cost
Crisis in Healthcare

1.0
Overview

By Dan Michelson

Any debate about the rising cost of healthcare quickly devolves into a search for the villain. The key culprit might be identified as the greedy pharmaceutical firm, the heartless insurance provider, or the overzealous regulator choking innovation and the free market at every turn. Unfortunately, the search for single villain predictably comes up empty as there isn't one. The debate ends with marginal insight into the core issues and limited solutions for bending the cost curve. However, the one thing that all stakeholders agree on is that left unchecked, healthcare cost inflation threatens to derail the economy. Annual healthcare costs in the U.S. have passed the $3 trillion mark nationally and individual health systems now confront ever-narrowing margins and a reimbursement environment in flux.

According to a recent survey conducted by the Healthcare Information Management Systems Society (HIMSS), reducing the cost of care has become the number one strategic concern for providers. Top line growth is no longer assumed. Bundled payment models and new models of care in general are upending the old world fee-for-service model – in which the way out of any fiscal problem was to simply do more. Now margins matters and managing cost will be the new normal. Cost reduction targets for some organizations are in the hundreds of millions of dollars, but most efforts are falling short.

Driving out cost is a big challenge for a number of reasons. First, there is little, if any, consensus around what constitutes cost. According to a recent survey, nine of 10 hospital executives have no understanding of cost. Part of the problem is that administrators, clinicians, payers and patients each have their own idea as to what defines cost. But even when there is consensus around what the term means, measuring it becomes an even larger, more perplexing issue. Simply put, reliable cost data is largely non-existent in healthcare.

That is why the move toward price transparency – a critical part of the conversation as the number of individuals on high-deductible plans accelerates – is often laced with confusion. News media accounts may highlight the extreme gaps between providers in the price of a given procedure. Yet context is often lacking. The figure on a hospital's charge master may have little bearing on what a patient will ultimately pay or what the hospital will ultimately receive.

For health system leaders, navigating this environment, let alone explaining it to patients, without accurate data can be all but impossible. In this section, we feature stories that illustrate why understanding and managing cost is so difficult for healthcare providers, highlighting the following:

- There is no common definition of cost in healthcare – p. 17

- Most hospital systems don't trust their data – p. 23

- Cost reduction efforts are coming up empty – p. 33

- Doctors don't have access to cost data – p. 40

- Cost data needs context – p. 43

- The business model is changing – p. 46

- Providers are facing uncomfortable questions – p. 52

- The cost of healthcare is complex – p. 55

1.1

What SpongeBob Can Teach Us About the Cost of Healthcare

By Dan Michelson

My 14-year old daughter made a huge mistake, which would horrify any teenager: She gave her father access to her Instagram account. As a tech geek, my real goal wasn't to check up on her (I swear), but rather to see whether the hype of Instagram matched the utility.

Instead what I found was the answer to a different and much more important question – why healthcare costs are such a mystery.

And here's the other twist. The answer came from one of the last places you would think – SpongeBob SquarePants.

One of the pictures on my daughter's Instagram was a cartoon of SpongeBob and his starfish friend Patrick staring at a ton of mattresses stacked as high as you can see in a never-ending warehouse.

SpongeBob says to Patrick, "Wow Patrick, look at all of these mattresses! How many do you think there are?"

Patrick replies, "Ten."

SpongeBob responds, "Cool."

While it was clear that there weren't only 10 mattresses in the warehouse, likely closer to 10,000, to SpongeBob it didn't matter. He asked for an answer and he got one. That was enough.

Then it hit me. This was the exact same conversation that happens in healthcare everywhere, every day.

The cost of healthcare is such a mystery that when you ask "what does it cost?" any number will do.

> *The cost of healthcare is such a mystery that when you ask "what does it cost?" any number will do.*

We have all heard stories where the price of a biopsy is $8,000 at one provider and only $800 at another. While that is uncomfortable to address, as price becomes transparent and reimbursement becomes more fixed, what is making providers more nervous is that they aren't able to answer whether or not they are making money in either scenario.

In other words, if they don't know their own cost they don't know their margins either, which makes it impossible to price with any level of confidence.

Why is this so confusing?

There are really two core issues – a lack of definition and a lack of information.

Issue #1: We have no idea what each other is talking about

All experienced stakeholders know that cost is the elephant in the room, but the topic is incredibly confusing.

Here's how it plays out in the hospital setting. When administrators and clinicians are discussing cost, some are talking about charges, some price, some reimbursement and some real, true cost. To make it even more challenging, each one of those definitions would differ dramatically if patients or payers were in the room.

For payers, you could be referring to Medicare/Medicaid vs. private pay. Within private pay, of course, there are hundreds of insurance plans and then within each plan are many different options. And for patients, once an option is selected, when one talks about cost, they could be referring to their payroll deduction, deductible or co-pay.

If you were to create a matrix for what I described, you would have to fill in a few dozen boxes, each with a different definition, and then agree on the one you are talking about.

Because of this complexity, the subject of cost is often misunderstood or ignored altogether.

The simple recommendation is to clearly define what element (which box in the matrix) you are talking about before the conversation begins. At the very least, SpongeBob and Patrick were looking at the same pile of mattresses. In that light, they were one step ahead of U.S. healthcare.

Once you implement a clear definition of cost, you will realize you now have a bigger problem – a lack of accessible, reliable cost data. That's where SpongeBob and Patrick fell short, and this brings us to the second issue.

Issue #2: Reliable cost data doesn't exist in healthcare – we're flying blind

Following the recommendation to focus on just one aspect and one definition of cost, let's focus on cost from a provider's perspective. As confirmed in a recent study by the Health Information Management Systems Society, the cost of healthcare has now become the No. 1 strategic priority for providers.

And this is a problem because most providers have no access to reliable cost data. As outlined in a recent article in the Harvard Business Review by Michael Porter, "When it comes to the cost of healthcare, providers are flying blind."

What's driving the need to understand and take action on cost data? The primary driver is the shift toward capitated or bundled payment models. A fixed payment structure is flipping the business model for healthcare upside down. As the top line becomes fixed and costs continue to rise, providers are shifting their focus to the bottom line, from a clinical and a financial perspective. Margins now matter.

This is where real cost comes into play as healthcare providers now need to understand their margins like any other business. The uncomfortable question that is making the knees wobbly of every CFO is, "When you go to negotiate a bundled care agreement, do you know if you are making or losing money?"

The answer for most is that they really don't know. And even when they think they know their cost, they are typically referring to charges. They are truly flying blind.

A recent survey of finance executives from over 200 hospitals in over 30 states by Strata Decision Technology found less than 10 percent of hospitals have timely access to accurate and complete cost data. Clearly this is a black hole that needs to be filled, which is leading many organizations to implement advanced cost accounting applications.

Clearly 10 mattresses was not accurate, but SpongeBob accepted that answer. In the bottom of the ocean, this might be okay. However, with $3 trillion in the mix and one-third of hospitals operating with negative margins, administrators and clinicians can't fly blind any longer. They must demand access to accurate cost data. Otherwise they will be deep in the ocean and they will drown, as many are already experiencing right now.

While cost accounting applied correctly will give providers the data they need, many believe that even if clinicians were given that information, they wouldn't understand it or use it. Turns out, that is a myth.

Dispelling the myth: Doctors actually want and will use cost information

As the bias goes, doctors don't care about cost and won't take action if they had the information. The data says otherwise.

A recent study was published in *Health Affairs* where 503 orthopedic surgeons and residents at Duke University, Harvard University, the University of Maryland, Mayo Clinic, the University of Pennsylvania, Stanford University and Washington University in St. Louis were asked to estimate the costs of 13 commonly used orthopedic devices. If their response was within 20 percent of the actual cost (a pretty large variance), the answer was considered correct.

> *As the bias goes, doctors don't care about cost and won't take action if they had the information. The data says otherwise.*

Physicians responded correctly only 20 percent of the time, as they lack access to that data. However, 80 percent of these same physicians indicated that they thought cost should be considered in the decision-making process for devices. Clearly there is an opportunity to fill that gap with real and actionable data.

Another study, conducted at the University of Miami and published in *Archives of Surgery,* helps dispel the myth that if doctors had cost data they won't do anything with it. In this study, a weekly announcement of the cost to non-intensive care unit patients for lab services during the prior week was sent to surgical house staff and attending physicians. The end result was a 25 percent reduction in the volume of routine blood work.

So, while it is easy to dismiss this interaction between SpongeBob and Patrick as nothing more than a cartoon, it is better used as a cautionary tale. All providers need to ask themselves if the conversation SpongeBob and Patrick were having at the bottom of the ocean is really any different than the ones about the cost of care we are having in healthcare every day.

Providing timely access to accurate and complete cost data will unleash an opportunity for all of us to be better stewards of our significant, yet finite resources and build a better system of health and healthcare.

Republished, with permission, from Becker's Hospital Review, April 29, 2015.

1.2

CFOS' Fatal Flaw: Survey Finds 9 of 10 Hospital Executives Don't Know Their Cost

By Strata Decision Technology & *Becker's Healthcare*

A recent survey of 100 hospital and healthcare delivery system executives conducted by Strata Decision Technology and *Becker's Healthcare*, found that 90 percent of those responsible for care don't know the cost of it. This gap is driving the rapid adoption of more advanced cost accounting applications that make data more accurate, accessible and actionable.

CFOs are now recognizing this simple, fatal flaw — how can you manage cost if the people responsible for it have no access to information? Recognizing that over $3.2 trillion is spent on healthcare in the U.S. every year, with over $1 trillion flowing through hospitals, the lack of tools to effectively understand and manage the cost of care represents a black hole of stunning proportions.

The end result is that most CFOs are left to manage the cost crisis in the pitch dark. The typical CFO for a U.S. healthcare delivery system is managing the financial engine for a multibillion-dollar business with thousands of employees and razor-thin operating margins that average 2 percent. They are seeing their core inpatient business declining in volume by close to 3 percent per year over the last five years. With that said, their biggest challenge ahead is that their already shaky business model is being flipped upside down with the introduction of capitated and bundled payment programs that hold hospital systems accountable for taking on the risk of a fixed top line.

With margins this thin, growth this challenging and a future this uncertain, you would quickly conclude that understanding and managing cost would be mission critical.

Surprisingly, over 90 percent of U.S. hospitals either don't have a cost accounting system or have one that is outdated and insufficient. And physicians and other clinicians whose decisions control roughly 80 percent of a hospital's total spending are provided with little to no information on cost. The end result is a lack of accurate and actionable cost data that has made consistently understanding, managing and driving out cost close to impossible.

Understanding expenses in a hospital is complex. Hospitals consume and produce a staggering amount of services and products every day, ranging from 12,000 to 45,000 individual items. Implementing and maintaining sophisticated costing models on this scale has been challenging. With that said, one of the primary issues has been the flawed model of using a ratio of cost to charge (RCC) methodology to estimate cost. This standard has proven to be inaccurate due to its flawed premise, because the actual cost of a product or service doesn't necessarily correlate to what you charge for that item in any industry. For example, if you sold a cup of coffee for $2.00 and used an RCC of 75 cents, your estimate of cost would be $1.50 and your margin would be 50 cents. But if you decided to raise the price to $4.00, your costs wouldn't automatically go up to $3.00. If you cut the cost to $1.00, your costs wouldn't fall to 75 cents. It's easy to see how inaccurate this approach would be for any business interested in understanding their true cost or margin.

In healthcare, where the hospital chargemaster is seen as a black box and what providers actually charge for an item is often more art than science, the current standard of applying a RCC to estimate cost often leads to inaccurate conclusions, leaving few hospital administrators with the ability to have any understanding of their true operating margins.

In addition to the recognition of the flaws of the current approach, the need to understand cost is also increasing due to market pressures. Hospital systems' growing participation in capitated or risk-based payment models is driving organizations to see value in gaining a deeper understanding of their clinical data and true costs, as well as how those data sets interact. In these new models, the need to understand margin is very clear. Without accurate costing data, healthcare organizations are flying blind in these agreements and deciding how to improve processes, redesign care and drive value is extraordinarily difficult.

Recognizing the operational issues that need to be solved and the strategic value of understanding cost, hospital system CFOs are moving quickly to implement advanced cost accounting applications that provide accurate, accessible and actionable information on the cost of care delivery for their organization.

This report examines the state of cost accounting in hospital systems today, including organizations' current cost accounting capabilities as well as their preparedness for costing in value-based payment structures. It then provides an overview of the movement to implement advanced cost accounting and identifies five factors driving hospital system CFOs to put new systems in place.

Methodology

This research draws on a survey conducted in May 2017 of 100 healthcare finance, operations and clinical leaders by Strata Decision Technology and *Becker's Healthcare*. The survey set out to evaluate cost accounting practices at healthcare provider organizations nationwide. Survey participants represented a range of provider types, including large academic medical centers, regional health systems, children's hospitals and independent community hospitals. About 40 percent of respondents held financial roles within their organizations.

The current state of Cost Accounting in U.S. hospitals and healthcare delivery systems

Cost accounting is not new to healthcare. Yet the complexity of modern hospital systems — composed of various inpatient and outpatient departments, staff, physicians, payer relationships, contracts and service lines — makes understanding costs in this environment particularly challenging.

The Strata/*Becker's* survey and associated research identified three common issues in hospital cost accounting that need to be addressed.

Current cost accounting methods are seen as inaccurate and the information isn't used

Compared to other industries, healthcare has been slow to adopt more sophisticated forms of advanced cost accounting, such as activity-based costing, cost study-based costing, physician costing and pharmacy costing. The Strata/*Becker's* survey found that while roughly 70 percent of hospitals practice some form of cost accounting, only one in 10 currently incorporate more advanced costing methods.

Instead, most organizations today — 90 percent — rely on rudimentary costing approaches, such as the ratio of costs to charges, according to a 2016 report from the *Healthcare Financial Management Association*. Basic costing methods like RCC are relatively straightforward and require little capital or managerial investment to complete. However, their accuracy at approximating costs is questionable at best, resulting in the data rarely being used. A Boston University study found for more than 30 percent of DRGs, average RCC-calculated costs differed from estimates made by more sophisticated methods by over 10 percent.

Most hospital systems aren't able to define cost across the care continuum

Basic costing methods allow providers to aggregate and analyze costs at the specialty or service department level. However, these systems don't have the ability to facilitate a deeper or more nuanced understanding of costs, such as the costs of treating individual patients with specific medical conditions over their full cycle of care.

The Strata/*Becker's* survey found less than 15 percent of hospital systems report having the ability to look at total cost across the full care continuum.

In fact, most hospital systems struggle to accurately estimate costs for providing care within their respective facilities. According to a 2016 HIMSS survey, less than one-third of provider organizations reported having the ability to evaluate the actual cost to deliver care or the profit margin necessary per service line to maintain financial health.

> *Less thank 15% of hospitals can look at cost across the continuum.*

Most hospital systems don't trust their data

Only 12 percent of hospital leaders report having high confidence in the accuracy of their cost information, according to the Strata/*Becker's* survey. While most healthcare organizations have a formal process for determining cost, only 39 percent of organizations reported regularly reviewing costs to ensure their data is current. Due to this and the recognition of the flaws of the RCC methodology, end users often don't trust the data and aren't incorporating it into their daily workflow.

Ensuring financial leaders use high-quality data to support clinical and strategic decision-making is critical. Feeding low-quality data into analytics or using inaccurate data to drive decision-making can produce the wrong conclusion and negatively affect patient care and financial performance. With that said, many hospitals still continue to run a costing process, producing data that no one uses and leading to a waste of time and resources.

Understanding the benefits of Advanced Cost Accounting

Over the last five years, legacy cost accounting systems are increasingly being replaced by Advanced Cost Accounting applications that provide accurate, accessible and actionable cost information. Advanced Cost Accounting includes a set of methodologies including time-based, activity-based costing (ABC), as well as supply-based and pharmacy-based costing, cost study and relative value unit (RVU) based costing. One methodology alone is not sufficient to consistently and accurately understand cost in healthcare. Healthcare is very different from other industries due to the data that is available, the variety of patient conditions, physician preferences, site of care, as well as the non-homogeneity of expenses and how they are tracked. Cost accounting needs to be accurate and comprehensive, but most importantly it has to be a scalable process.

Advanced Cost Accounting helps address these issues. Expenses are categorized and attributed to patients based on the most practical and accurate methodology available to a provider organization. It provides a library of approaches based on the setting as well as data available to automate the process, such as EHR-based time stamps. The focus is on all the potential opportunities for identifying variation while ensuring the effort is worth the output. Leveraging a data-driven approach reduces the need for manual intervention to identify costs and enables organizations to identify true cost variation for every patient.

More advanced costing methods also take into account additional costs that are not always included in the summation of charges on a hospital bill, such as the cost to treat surgical site infections or "invisible" choices and processes during treatments as well as waste. This "Swiss Army Knife" toolset of multiple methodologies is quickly becoming the new standard.

Advanced cost accounting incorporates a variety of clinical and financial data going beyond the traditional charges and volume information. The sources that form the building blocks of advanced cost accounting are from across the continuum of care and provide drivers to accurately attribute costs to patient activity include the following:

- Payroll

- Physician billing activity

- Post-acute activity

- Surgical detail

- Chargeable and non-chargeable supply detail

- Pharmacy detail and pricing (340B variation)

- Patient clinical and demographic detail

- EHR time stamps

- Order set detail

Key drivers behind the shift to Advanced Cost Accounting applications

Market forces are driving the need for hospitals to understand their costs at a deeper and more actionable level. As systems move toward population health management and expand into clinically integrated networks, hospitals feel the urgency to understand the actual costs associated with specific patients and particular procedures. Otherwise, changes in utilization patterns could have significant and unintended consequences on hospitals' bottom lines.

The Strata/*Becker's* research identified the key factors driving hospital systems to adopt advanced cost accounting solutions in preparation for value-based medicine.

Understanding true margins

Advanced costing methodologies can give hospital system leaders visibility into an organization's true margins on an episode or service line basis by accounting for additional costs accrued after the point of service. As more providers take on risk, they are increasingly exposed from a financial perspective. Understanding their margins as they negotiate, which over 90 percent of hospitals can't do today, is only the first step. Once they put that contract in motion, they need to understand the variation by physician for every patient they treat and for every procedure they perform.

39 percent of hospitals regularly review and update their cost data.

Identifying opportunities to reduce cost

As changes to the healthcare business model increasingly place emphasis on outcomes-based reimbursement, it is important for hospital and health system leaders to ensure their respective organizations take advantage of the appropriate technologies to both eliminate wasteful expenditures and ensure patients receive optimal care. Using advanced costing methodologies that incorporate quality data for a specific procedure, such as knee replacements, hospital systems can track and identify which types of adverse clinical variations are most costly to the organization over a period of time. Armed with this knowledge — as well as the data to back it up — financial and clinical leaders can target the greatest cost-cutting opportunities while also improving patient outcomes.

Viewing the total cost of care across the continuum from both inpatient and outpatient settings

As care migrates to outpatient settings, the ability to integrate and understand costing outside an organization's four walls is increasingly important. Traditional cost accounting systems often don't have the flexibility to integrate cost data from affiliated organizations outside the hospital setting, such as physician practices and post-acute providers. Some hospital systems have focused on understanding costs of care in a particular setting, such as an inpatient admission for acute myocardial infarction or for a specific surgical procedure. Understanding costs for units of care will remain critical. However, holistic payment necessitates understanding costs across organizations and care settings and, often, over long periods of time. Advanced cost accounting solutions integrate with other data sources to provide a cross-continuum view. Once hospital systems understand costs and quality outcomes across the entire episode of care — from inpatient admission to 90 days post-discharge — they can begin forming a financial and clinical strategy for effectively participating in bundled payment models.

Sharing the financial impact of harm events and variations in clinical care

Clinical and financial leaders at Yale New Haven (Conn.) Health System (YNHHS) developed Quality Variation Indicators (QVIs) to examine how clinical variation affects case cost and overall margins for specific procedures. Specifically, QVIs help to identify cases in which patients experience potentially preventable variations in quality, such as a surgical site infection, and assess the effect on patient care and case cost. YNHHS tracks nearly 30 QVI categories, including central line-associated blood stream infections, deep vein thrombosis, readmission and perioperative pulmonary embolism. YNHHS found incorporating QVIs into case costing increased total costs between 300 and 400 percent on average compared to cases without QVIs. Using this costing method, the organization determined it was spending more than expected over a single episode due to clinical variation while earning the same net revenue, resulting in a considerably smaller profit margin. QVIs are one type of advanced case costing helping both clinical and financial leaders root out and understand indirect drivers of cost variations. This balanced view of performance is central to reducing variation and competing in a value-based care setting, and is a major driver in the movement toward advanced cost accounting.

Accessing accurate cost information more quickly and frequently

The reliance on older, inefficient cost accounting systems has caused most organizations to run their costing process just once or twice per year, in many cases. Additionally, when they run costing, the process often takes a number of days to complete due to the size of the data and legacy costing applications' lack of sophistication. Hospitals can gain several benefits from running costing more frequently. Running daily or weekly costing processes supports financial, clinical and operational decision-making by ensuring department leaders have the most current and reliable data on hand. Advanced cost accounting systems also have costing engines capable of modeling costs using multiple methodologies — such as RVUs, ABC, time-driven ABC and supply acquisition cost — for more accurate, reliable conclusions. More advanced systems that can run the costing process in minutes versus days or hours.

Creating an integrated approach to financial planning and performance

With an accurate costing process in place, providers can roll out a more integrated approach to financial planning. Providers can identify cost savings opportunities via cost accounting methods, put programs in motion and then adjust long-range financial plans and operating budgets to ensure the cost savings stick. Augusta (Ga.) University Health System is one such organization that has made cost accounting part of an integrated financial performance approach. The two-hospital system recently engaged in strategic planning for a new 100-bed hospital and leaders needed reliable, valid data to confidently plan for the future. Specifically, system leaders wanted to calculate spatial needs per department based on clinical growth projections. They also needed to predict how adding services at the new facility would affect volumes at their flagship and outpatient locations.

However, financial and growth reports crunched by different teams revealed different data, causing hospital system leaders to question the data's accuracy. Augusta's business leaders realized they needed an accurate method to calculate the true cost of a surgical case and turned to an advanced cost accounting solution for answers. Augusta first implemented advanced costing in its perioperative services unit, including an adult operating room, a children's hospital operating room, labor and delivery, a cardiac catheterization lab and a digestive health center. By combining cost data with financial data in the decision support system, executives gained visibility into costs and margins per episode of care and identified true cost drivers. In the past, $10 million in equipment and labor costs were distributed among all OR cases. Advanced costing enabled financial leaders to attribute that cost to specific procedure codes and cases, changing the true margins across various surgical lines. Executives then extrapolated from this information to understand overall business and patient trends for long-term strategic planning. The team uses this data to determine whether to accept or reject business proposals. Now, Augusta's system CFO, Vice President of facilities and directors of marketing and outreach meet regularly to incorporate market share, volume projections and other data into long-term plans.

Conclusion

In the past, cost accounting has been undervalued and underutilized as accuracy and accessibility of information on cost wasn't seen as a necessity in traditional volume-driven payment models. This is not the case in risk- or value-based medicine. Without credible and detailed cost data, it will be extraordinarily difficult for healthcare organizations to strategically manage their operations and minimize the impact of declining reimbursement.

With close to 90 percent of healthcare leaders operating in the dark on cost, leveraging data from advanced cost accounting that is comprehensive, accurate and accessible is mission critical. Providers are then able to collaborate and make more informed decisions in order and ultimately deliver more value to the patients and the community that they serve.

Republished, with permission, from Becker's Hospital Review, October 11, 2017.

1.3

The Current State of Cost Reduction in Healthcare

By Liz Kirk

Close to $2.8 trillion[1], or one of every five dollars in the United States, is spent on healthcare every year. Close to $765 billion[2] is considered wasted due to over utilization, redundancy, inefficiency, medical errors and unnecessary variation in clinical practice.

According to the HIMSS Healthcare Provider Innovation Survey, reducing the total cost of care has become the number one strategic concern for healthcare providers. This is being driven by significant downward pressure on revenue from declining patient volumes, change in payer mix, unfavorable case mix, a shift to high deductible plans increasing the burden on patients, and a fundamental shift in reimbursement models towards bundled or capitated agreements.

A recent report from Standard & Poor's looked at average operating margins for 138 healthcare delivery systems. The data showed that hospitals' margins are contracting for the first time since 2008 with the average operating margin dropping to 2.2 percent. One-third of hospitals currently have negative operating margins[3]. The clear

---

1   Centers for Medicare and Medicaid

2   Institute of Medicine

3   American Hospital Association

implication is that costs are rising faster than revenue and that a new approach is needed.

The end result is that most healthcare delivery systems are now implementing cost improvement programs with targets that exceed $100 million. To date, most of these initiatives are falling short. Since the traditional focus has been on revenue or the top line, providers lack the competencies to identify cost savings opportunities, implement them effectively, and ensure that they stick. Due to this, providers have often turned to consulting firms for help, but while these initiatives provide some level of one-time savings, they don't provide an ongoing continuous cost improvement program or process.

Strata Decision Technology recently distributed a survey about cost reduction to healthcare finance professionals at providers across the country. The brief survey was designed to address not only organizations' goals related to cost reduction, but also to identify the key challenges that are keeping many from achieving their savings targets.

The survey was completed by 100 individuals in finance from 75 organizations, including large academic medical centers, regional health systems, children's hospitals and independent community hospitals.

Cost Reduction Initiatives

Organization Has a Cost Reduction Target In Place

88%

Organization is Successful at Reaching Cost Reduction Target

17%

Summary of cost reduction findings

According to the survey, 88 percent of healthcare organizations have set cost reduction targets. The prevalence of cost reduction targets shows that most providers are taking action in order to maintain margins. Providers recognize that only those who can reduce and re-allocate resources to match changing volumes and eliminate inefficient practices will maintain their already narrow margins.

While providers are taking action relative to driving out cost, they are often falling short of their targets. 83 percent of healthcare organizations with cost reduction targets reported that they are not achieving their cost savings goals. Close to 70 percent of respondents with cost reduction targets report that their efforts are yielding minimal cost savings.

The opportunity to realize cost savings decreases as the cost reduction program progresses from identifying savings opportunities to validating savings to implementing the opportunities and then tracking and maintaining the savings. Often the opportunities that have been identified lack the depth or breadth, the savings is not actionable, or the implementation is not executed well.

The survey results indicate that healthcare providers are facing many obstacles when it comes to achieving real cost savings. At the core of these challenges is the need for a new mindset, skillset and toolset to effectively drive out costs.

Fifty-five percent of the respondents found it difficult to quantify and track savings and 44 percent said that keeping track of multiple initiatives and projects related to cost reduction presents many challenges, which is most likely because it is time-consuming and data intensive. Forty-four percent also reported that a lack of accountability for driving out cost was holding their organization back.

Additional issues providers are facing include a lack of engagement from clinicians and operations, a lack of staff to lead improvement projects and a lack of focus from senior leaders. In addition, 27 percent of survey respondents reported that their improvement projects are not yielding measurable savings, but rather either "soft dollar savings" or no savings at all.

Challenges with Cost Reduction Initiatives

29%	Lack of engagement from clinical/operations
44%	Lack of accountability for results
30%	Inconsistent focus from senior leaders
25%	Lack of staff to lead projects
11%	Difficult to know how much cost to take out
27%	Improvements don't produce measurable savings
44%	Difficult to keep track of multiple projects and initiatives
55%	Difficult to quantify and track savings
20%	Hard to find opportunities to reduce costs

Conclusion

Just as quality improvement became a focus for healthcare providers over the last decade, effective cost improvement must become a core competency for organizations in order to meet their financial targets in support of effectively serving their patients and their communities.

Today many hospitals and health systems are falling short because they are not equipped with the right mindset, toolset and skillset to achieve their cost savings targets and to maintain that savings over time. Unlike revenue cycle management, there are limited competencies, tools or applications to help support cost improvement programs or even one-time cost reduction initiatives.

With hundreds of billions of dollars of unnecessary spending, the opportunity to drive out cost will emerge as a major opportunity for hospitals and healthcare delivery systems. With this we will begin to see the emergence of more advanced cost accounting tools, to help understand cost, and the introduction of a new category of software applications that can help organizations drive cost out on a continuous basis. These applications will focus on improving efficiency, reducing variation and eliminating waste.

The end result is that cost reduction will be seen as a more strategic, ongoing process that is cross-functional, informed by accurate data, and that drives action towards hard dollar savings. This will benefit both patients and providers as resources will be used to increase value and improve overall outcomes.

Based on a survey of large academic medical centers, regional health systems, children's hospitals and independent community hospitals across the U.S. Strata Decision Technology, August 2014.

DOCTORS DON'T
HAVE ACCESS
TO COST DATA

1.4

Doctors Don't Know and Don't Care About Costs? That's Half Right.

By Dan Michelson

Having been in healthcare for over 20 years, I have heard many times from many people that "doctors don't know and don't care about the cost of healthcare."

Like many things that we hear over and over, we begin to believe they are true. In this case, it turns out this one actually is true. Well, at least it's half true.

The data will surprise you

Two recent studies have found that doctors know very little about cost. But that same research has also confirmed that, contrary to the popular narrative, doctors actually do care about cost.

Recently a study was published in *Health Affairs* where 503 orthopedic surgeons and residents at Duke University, Harvard University, the University of Maryland, Mayo Clinic, the University of Pennsylvania, Stanford University and Washington University in St. Louis were asked to estimate the costs of thirteen commonly used orthopedic devices.

Here's the part that was really interesting. If their response was within 20 percent of the actual cost (a pretty large variance), the answer was considered to be correct. What's shocking is that even with that buffer, physicians were correct only 20 percent of the time. In other words, as stated above, as it relates to cost, doctors don't know.

So, this leads to the second part of the headline, 'Do doctors care actually care about cost?' In the same study referenced above, those same doctors were asked whether they thought cost should be considered in the decision-making process for devices.

Two different studies of over 500 physicians with the same conclusion – physicians do care about cost.

Eighty percent said 'yes.' It turns out they do care.

And that isn't an isolated data point. Last year, Bain & Company conducted a survey and asked 502 physicians a similar question – do they agree with the following statement, "I feel it is part of my responsibility as a physician to help bring healthcare costs under control."

Incredibly their response was identical to the first study – 80 percent of physicians agreed that they were responsible for keeping costs under control.

So, two different studies of over 500 physicians with the same conclusion – physicians do care about cost.

Doctors won't do anything with the data, right?

The concern I hear many express is that while physicians say they want the information, they won't do anything with it. It turns out this one is wrong as well.

Two studies provide data points that counteract that argument.

The first, published in *JAMA Internal Medicine*, was conducted at Johns Hopkins University. Physicians were presented with cost information on order sets via their electronic health records at the point of care in real time. During the study, the test group saw a 10 percent reduction in test order volume translating to over $400,000 in incremental savings versus the control group where cost information was not presented.

And, surprisingly, it doesn't matter if cost data is provided in real time, while the decision is being made, or retrospectively. A second study, conducted at the University of Miami and published in *Archives of Surgery*, took a retrospective approach.

In this study, a weekly announcement of the dollar amount charged to non-intensive care unit patients for lab services during the prior week was sent to surgical house staff and attending physicians. In this case they saw a 25 percent reduction in the dollars charged per patient per day for routine blood work.

Taken together, these two studies reach the same conclusion – if you provide cost information to physicians, they will take action and drive down cost.

A $2 trillion opportunity

It has been estimated that doctors control 60-80 percent of the cost of care with the decisions that they make: medications, devices, hospitals, whether to pursue surgery or therapy, etc. As our healthcare spend as a nation is fast approaching $3 trillion per year, this would mean physicians control roughly $1.8 to $2.4 trillion of that spend. And they do it with no information on cost.

Clearly there is an enormous opportunity to change the game regarding the cost of healthcare, but it will require providing physicians with not just the clinical information they need to make better decisions via an EHR, but the cost information they require via advanced financial decision support solutions, specifically advanced cost accounting applications.

They don't know about cost, but they want to know. They do care about cost and they will take action if we provide them the information.

And everyone will win when they do.

Republished, with permission, from Healthcare IT News, February 20, 2014.

1.5

Cost Data Needs Context to be Meaningful

By Karen Wagner

According to a *Health Affairs* article, when orthopedic surgeons at six major health systems were asked to identify the cost of 13 commonly used orthopedic devices, fewer than one in five could estimate the actual cost within 20 percent accuracy. Further, despite a common narrative that doctors are only concerned about outcomes, more than 80 percent of those same doctors said if they had access to the information, they would consider cost as one of the key criteria in choosing a device.

Cost data need context to be meaningful

"Presenting cost data without a quality or clinical context doesn't go very far," said Dan Michelson, CEO of Strata Decision Technology. "In the past, either cost data wasn't presented, or it was presented without context, and that is a really big deal." Michelson commented on the intersection of cost and quality data during a presentation at ANI: The 2016 *HFMA* National Institute. Other presenters included Stephen Allegretto, vice president of financial planning, Yale New Haven Hospital; Keith Churchwell, MD, vice president of cardiovascular services, Yale New Haven Health System; and Mary O'Connor, MD, director of the Musculoskeletal Center at Yale School of Medicine and Yale New Haven Hospital.

Delivering relevant cost data

Cost can mean many different things to different people. For some, it might mean price, and to others the amount reimbursed, and for yet others the actual hard cost of an item along with the allocated hard labor that goes with it. To make cost information useful among clinical staff, healthcare organizations should develop a method for delivering cost information that is consistent and provides context for clinicians.

Health systems also should not take a one-size-fits-all approach to the method of delivering cost data. There are several methods to provide these data to doctors, including via reports, contained in order sets, as a tool clinicians can use to look up data, and as part of the review process when the care team is conducting cost studies on specific procedures.

"It is no different than how quality data are presented," Michelson said. "It should be incorporated in many different ways throughout the organization."

Combining cost and clinical data

Leveraging cost data with clinical data in a hospital's electronic medical record is how health systems can gain a true and accurate measure of value. Value is mathematically defined as quality—which is a combination of clinical quality and patient experience—over cost. The bottom part of the equation, the cost, allows hospitals to look at variations in quality and marry the cost data to see the financial effect of poor-quality care.

"This is not information that would have interested people just a couple of years ago," Michelson said. "But now that they understand this intersection of quality and cost is what defines value, people in finance recognize they need to understand this and also be the ones driving out this information."

Implementing the move to value

As Michelson described, moving to this model of creating value takes three elements. First, to get doctors on board, the staff at Yale shared information about topline revenue about the declining revenue per discharge—a trend that is occurring across the industry. Second, most health systems will likely need to add dedicated staff with the specific skill set to collect and manage these data while leveraging it across the organization. Third, is an investment in IT that will allow staff to manage the workflow for generating the data. This includes automating the generation of variation data that can be tracked and acted upon quickly.

"People have made the statement in the past that quality care is lower cost, but there was never data to back that up," Michelson said. "Now, with the work Yale has done, there is."

Republished, with permission, from the HFMA Newsletter, June 27, 2016.
Three Westbrook Corporate Center, Suite 600, Westchester, IL 60154-5732.
For more information, call 800-252-HFMA or vist hfma.org.

1.6

CFOs Look Into the Crystal Ball: The Future Business Model of Healthcare

By Karen Wagner

Hospitals and health systems must react faster to the quickening pace of change in healthcare by innovating and adapting their business model - or they probably won't survive.

That cautionary note was the overall theme delivered by CFOs from Wake Forest Baptist Medical Center, the University of Virginia Medical Center, and ProMedica during a standing-room only session on "Creating Healthcare's Future Business Model" moderated by Strata Decision Technology CEO, Dan Michelson, during the *Becker's Hospital Review* 8th Annual National Meeting in Chicago.

Panelists contended that the traditional business strategy that health systems have relied upon, centralized on maximizing inpatient revenue streams from a steady stream market of customers, won't be enough and won't be around to keep the doors open in the not-so-distant future.

The CFOs zeroed in on four key strategies they believe are essential to incorporate into business models to enable healthcare organizations to thrive:

- Aligning with other healthcare organizations

- Shifting from revenue cycle management to margin and outcomes management

- Developing new revenue streams

- Embracing a consumer-based model

Aligning with other healthcare organizations

Although every market offers a different environment for alignment, partnerships enable the disparate organizations to create leverage and capitalize on each other's strengths, said CFO Michael Browning of Toledo, Ohio-based ProMedica health system. Alignment doesn't necessarily mean mergers or acquisitions. Browning referred to a partnership between WakeMed Health & Hospitals, Raleigh, N.C., where he previously served as CFO, and Duke University Hospital, Durham, N.C., that combines the organizations' cardiology service lines into one program, which provides the opportunity to improve quality and service and reduce costs.

"I think that was a very innovative way to look at it," Browning said. "Organizations have to give up on some of those things that have historically been important to us, like our sole independence, and look at how we can provide the best healthcare while making sure that we're meeting all the needs of the people in our community."

Other partnerships may involve consolidating business functions, such as the revenue cycle. "I think those are types of joint ventures that many organizations will be working on in the future," he said.

Chad Eckes, CFO of Wake Forest Baptist Medical Center, an academic medical center in Winston-Salem, N.C., likened merger and acquisition activity in the healthcare industry to the previous period of mass consolidations in the banking industry. The trend in healthcare, driven by this need for back office improvement, can also be achieved through other forms of partnering, such as outsourcing, he said. Wake Forest Baptist just completed an outsourcing arrangement for physician billing services, which represents the fourth outsourcing arrangement completed since Eckes started with the organization about three years ago.

Shifting from revenue cycle management to margin and outcomes management

The participants were unanimous in their belief that the decades long focus on growing the top-line and revenue cycle management had run its course. Each CFO stated that over the next five years they believe that revenue cycle management will give way to margin and outcomes management.

Leveraging cost data together with clinical outcomes is central to measuring value.

One of the enabling technologies currently leveraged by all the organizations on the panel is advanced cost accounting and financial decision support. With this in place, organizations are able to understand both their true cost and margins, a critical set of data for both negotiating and performing effectively under bundled care contracts.

Leveraging that cost data together with clinical outcomes is central to measuring value, which is increasingly becoming the new currency for these organizations.

Developing new revenue streams

Healthcare delivery organizations are increasingly creating new streams of revenue from new sources, including non-patient services.

As providers become more proficient in population health management, marketing successful wellness programs to other providers can be a way to capitalize on existing expertise, said Nick Mendyka, CFO of the University of Virginia Health System, Charlottesville, VA. "We're the ones who provide that service, yet we're contracting with payers to do that work," Mendyka said. "So we can deliver wellness services in the vein of population health management and we can grow it, scale it, sell it to other smaller providers or employers."

Browning said traditional revenue sources will only be so helpful to the hospital's bottom line. To counter the loss in volume under value-based care, healthcare organizations have to gain access to the healthcare members' premium dollar. Value-based care is a central strategy but the long-term business model is still unclear, he contended. "It's the future, yet it's currently set up in a way where the insurance companies are the ones accruing the most benefit from all the great work everyone is doing. We've got to figure out how to create balance and share in that dollar as much as we can," Browning said.

ProMedica's insurance arm, Paramount, covers 350,000 lives and is "a major catalyst for our future," Browning said.

Embracing a consumer-based model

The panelists agreed that consumerism has changed and will continue to change the way healthcare is delivered and therefore managed. The approach to the market has changed dramatically in the past five years, Eckes said. "Back then, we didn't worry about consumer behavior, understanding buyer vs. non-buyer decision-making, or impacts of social media" he said. "We worried about referrals from physicians and having convenient ED's. Our customer is no longer just the patient and the referring physician. Our customer is now the employers, payers, family/friends of patients, and CIN's [clinically integrated network]." Such changes mean healthcare organizations have to be much more aware of the patient's desires, competition and patient experience.

"We have to articulate our value story and answer the questions of 'Why should the patient entrust their care to us. It's key to reinforce the quality that you should expect from the health system and the total patient experience that you'll get from us before, during and after'" the clinic or hospital visit, Eckes said.

Serving the consumer better also means price transparency, which requires healthcare organizations to have a better understanding of their cost structures, Mendyka said. Hospitals must be able to provide consumers with a more accurate estimate of their out-of-pocket costs, he said. "Whether that deductible is $1,000 or $15,000 there's still a greater likelihood that a patient will pay all or a portion of that bill when they know they're making the decision, they know what it costs," Mendyka said.

And, although no organization has yet to be 100 percent successful at this, finance managers have to fully understand their market segment and how patients choose providers. "It changes the equation and how we assess and set strategies," Mendyka said.

Redefining success

Overall, healthcare organizations, particularly finance departments, will have to redefine how they measure success. No longer will AA bond ratings be the sole determinant, Browning said.

"Ten years from now it's going to be more about what we do for our community. The quality we deliver, the service we deliver," he said.

Mendyka concurred. "The way that we're going to measure our organizations' or any individual's contributions is going to be very different in the future," he said. "It can be about community benefit. There will be new and very different things that we are going to be judged upon. Organizations must get ahead of this or they may not survive" he said.

These new success factors will mean making some tough business decisions, such as turning an acute care hospital into an outpatient center, Browning added. Healthcare leaders sometimes want to push such strategic decisions into the long-term future, but, he said, "The future is right here right now."

A peek at the future

Other strategies and trends noted by panelists at the *Becker's Hospital Review* 8th Annual Meeting:

- **Mike Browning, CFO, ProMedica:** In larger markets, more healthcare organizations will become integrated provider/payer entities, similar to the Kaiser Permanent model, where the provider portion becomes more or less the cost center of the organization.

- **Nick Mendyka, CFO, University of Virginia Medical Center:** Capital investment will be managed more strategically. As traditional revenue tightens, providers will have to compartmentalize revenue streams, tie costs to these programs, and then match strategic investment to revenue.

- **Chad Eckes, CFO, Wake Forest Baptist Medical Center:** Providers will have to become increasingly innovative to drive value. This means in the long-term healthcare organizations will turn to advanced technologies such as artificial intelligence to improve quality and reduce costs and blockchain to simplify the clinician credentialing process and "disintermediate" the payer process.

Republished, with permission, from Becker's Hospital Review, May 10, 2017.

1.7

The New Conversation in Healthcare: "What's Your Price . . . and Your Cost?"

By Dan Michelson

"Our average price for a total hip replacement is $34,866.03. And for that procedure, our average Medicare payment is $14,974.69, our average Medicaid payment is $9,583.80 and our average private insurance payment is $27,369.83."

Is this what the future looks like in the wake of the recent announcement of the proposed price transparency rule by the Centers for Medicare & Medicaid Services (CMS)?

Actually, this vision of tomorrow is the reality of today for a number of health systems, including the example above which you can find on the website for Spectrum Healthcare, a not-for-profit healthcare system in Michigan with 11 hospitals and 170 ambulatory and service sites.

But the pricing and payment information they have made available isn't just for total hip replacement procedures. It is right there on Spectrum's website for 44 inpatient procedures, 56 outpatient procedures and for 314 diagnostic procedures. And if you don't see the procedure you are looking for, you can call or send a secure message to a pricing specialist.

Clearly Spectrum is a first mover, but as the CMS rule is finalized, every health system's Board of Directors will be pushing the organization's executive teams to lead, not follow on this one.

Why?

With high-deductible health plans (HDHPs) being selected by 20 percent of individuals on employer-sponsored plans (up from 0 percent only a few years ago), it has become clear that conversations about cost with patients are going to be the new normal.

But the conversation on price is complex, because all stakeholders have different definitions of what the term price actually means. From the patients' perspective, price ultimately refers to their deductible and out of pocket cost. From a hospital's perspective, price is how much it charges. From a payer's perspective, price is what the payer negotiated.

Although those definitions will certainly be debated, hospitals and health systems all will acknowledge that they are struggling with the topic of pricing. A core concern for them is that, like any business, they cannot set their price effectively and responsibly without knowing their actual cost and, therefore, their margins. Yet in healthcare, most organizations simply don't have access to accurate cost data. So when it comes to pricing, they are flying blind.

The recognition of this cost data gap has resulted in a major movement to gain better access (data liquidity) to accurate cost data (data integrity) and then have the ability to drill into those data at a deeper, more actionable level (data density).

In this new environment, healthcare organizations require sophisticated cost accounting systems that enable them to understand cost and margins across service lines and across the entire continuum of care. Traditional cost accounting systems provide only inpatient cost and have significant issues relative to data accuracy and exceptionally poor access to data, often taking a week or longer to run a costing process. The end result is that most organizations only run costing once or twice a year.

Can you imagine executives in a healthcare system looking at clinical outcomes only once or twice a year? In today's world, this is unimaginable – and it should be similarly unimaginable for an organization to review data on its true cost and margins so infrequently. The simple fact is that healthcare providers require the data liquidity, integrity and density that are achievable with today's more advanced cost accounting systems to understand their cost and margins in support of developing a data-driven and effective pricing strategy.

The bottom line is that there is an underlying call to action attached to the CMS announcement. To prepare for the new conversation in healthcare, hospitals and health systems need to be able to price effectively, and to do so, they have to know their cost. Having this knowledge is not optional; it will be critical to an organization's survival and ability to remain competitive in the future.

Republished, with permission, from the hfm Healthcare Finance Blog, June 10, 2014.
Three Westbrook Corporate Center, Suite 600, Westchester, IL 60154-5732.
For more information, call 800-252-HFMA or visit hfma.org.

1.8

25 Things to Know About Healthcare Costs

By Ayla Ellison

From ACA mandates to baby boomers rapidly switching to Medicare, there are a number of factors influencing healthcare costs in the U.S.

Here are 25 things to know about those costs.

The difference between costs, charges and payments

1. Before delving into an analysis of healthcare costs, it is critical to understand the difference between healthcare costs, charges and payments. Hospital charges are essentially their list prices for medical services, which are different from hospitalization costs, or the actual amount of money insurers, patients or the government end up paying hospitals in exchange for services.

2. Hospital input costs are the costs a hospital incurs to provide care to a patient. This includes both variable costs (salaries of clinicians and costs of supplies and medications) and fixed costs (overhead expenses and cost of equipment, land and buildings), according to a report from The Advisory Board Company.

3. The prices on a hospital's chargemaster bear little relationship to the amount most patients are asked to pay. That's because

commercial insurers negotiate discounts with healthcare providers on behalf of their members, and Medicare and Medicaid set fixed payment rates for hospital services, which are often less than the actual cost of care. Additionally, most hospitals allow low-income patients to receive free care or care for a reduced charge.

4. Hospital list prices aren't completely irrelevant, however, as they usually serve as a starting point for negotiations with commercial payers.

5. Hospitals may use chargemasters to boost their finances. A study published in the September issue of *Health Affairs* suggests hospitals were using chargemaster prices to drive up revenue in 2013.

> *National healthcare spending is expected to grow at an average annual rate of 5.8 percent over the next decade, according to CMS.*

National healthcare spending

6. National healthcare spending grew 5.5 percent in 2015, reaching $3.2 trillion, according to estimates from CMS' Office of the Actuary published in July.

7. This growth marks an increase from 2014, when rapidly rising drug prices and health insurance expansion under the ACA drove spending upward 5.3 percent.

8. National healthcare spending is expected to grow at an average annual rate of 5.8 percent over the next decade, according to CMS.

9. From 2015 to 2025, health spending is projected to grow 1.3 percentage points faster than gross domestic product.

Medicare, Medicaid and CHIP spending

10. Spending for the major government healthcare programs will rise by nearly $55 billion, or about 6 percent, in 2016, and Medicare will account for more than half of that increase, according to

budget projections from the Congressional Budget Office.

11. Outlays for the Medicare program are expected to increase by $30 billion, or 6 percent, this year, with growth largely driven by increased spending per person on prescription drugs.

12. Medicaid outlays are expected to increase by $15 billion, or 4 percent, this year. The CBO anticipates Medicaid enrollment will be roughly flat in 2016.

13. The CBO estimates outlays for the Children's Health Insurance Program will climb $5 billion this year, to $14 billion.

Prescription drug costs

14. Prescription drug spending increased 12.2 percent to $297.7 billion in 2014, faster than the 2.4 percent growth in 2013, according to CMS.

15. Inpatient hospital drug costs increased by an average of 38.7 percent per admission between 2013 and 2015, according to an analysis from the independent research organization NORC at the University of Chicago.

16. According to a Kaiser Family Foundation poll, 82 percent of Americans want the federal government to negotiate with drug companies to get lower prices on medications for Medicare beneficiaries.

17. Seventy-eight percent of Americans support limiting the amount pharmaceutical companies can charge for high-cost drugs for illnesses like hepatitis or cancer, according to the KFF poll.

Out-of-pocket healthcare costs

18. In recent years, patients have become increasingly responsible for a greater share of their healthcare expenditures due to changes in health insurance policies.

19. Out-of-pocket spending on healthcare costs increased 2.1 percent in 2013. Due to expanded coverage through Medicaid and private insurance, out-of-pocket healthcare spending growth slowed to 1.3 percent in 2014, according to CMS.

20. In 2009, annual out-of-pocket spending on hospital care was $25.6 billion, according to the Peterson-Kaiser Health System Tracker. Out-of-pocket spending on hospital care steadily increased over the next three years, reaching $32.7 billion in 2013.

21. Annual out-of-pocket spending on hospital care fell 4.1 percent to $31.4 billion in 2014.

22. Out-of-pocket spending on prescription drugs increased 2.7 percent to $44.7 billion in 2014, according to CMS.

Costs broken down by hospital type

23. The average cost per inpatient day in 2014 at state/local government hospitals was $1,974, according to the latest statistics from Kaiser State Health Facts. That's up from $1,878 per inpatient day in 2013. These figures are an estimate of expenses incurred in a day of inpatient care and are adjusted higher to include an estimate of the volume of outpatient services, according to Kaiser State Health Facts.

24. The average cost per inpatient day in 2014 was $2,346 at nonprofit hospitals, compared to $2,289 per inpatient day the year prior.

25. The average cost per inpatient day at for-profit hospitals in 2014 was $1,798, up slightly from $1,791 per inpatient day in 2013.

Republished, with permission, from Becker's Hospital Review, October 25, 2016.

PART TWO

How Cost Accounting Became
the Next "Killer App"

2.0

Overview

By Liz Kirk

O ver the last 15 years, Electronic Health Records have become the "killer app" in healthcare…a must have for every healthcare provider. However, the shift to value-based care is driving hospitals and health systems to evaluate what additional systems to put in place to support this new model of care. Investments are being made in population health applications on the clinical side, but, until recently, there wasn't much clarity on how to prepare from a financial systems perspective.

Enter Advanced Cost Accounting…the first true "killer app" to hit the financial side of hospitals since the endless flurry of systems that were deployed over the last 40 years for revenue cycle management. Advanced Cost Accounting applications are quickly becoming central to understanding and delivering value. Understanding cost has shifted from a back room broken process to an urgent board room priority.

In this section, we provide an outline of the 10 reasons why hospitals are quickly shifting to advanced cost accounting applications including the need to understand the total cost of care across inpatient and outpatient settings. This broad perspective is becoming the gold standard as payers increasingly move to bundled payment arrangements, impose readmission penalties and reimburse based on outcomes. Financial and clinical performance become inextricably linked making an advanced cost accounting system an essential building block for competing from a financial perspective.

The stories that follow detail the value of shifting to new and better ways to understand cost, including:

- Use cost accounting as a killer app – p. 63

- Leverage cost accounting as a performance tool – p. 68

- Create a new mindset, skillset and toolset – p. 73

- Implement activity-based costing to pinpoint cost savings – p. 77

- Use dashboards to drive performance – p. 80

- Leverage decision support to improve planning – p. 86

2.1

Why Advanced Cost Accounting is Becoming the Next 'Killer App' for CFOs

By Dan Michelson

As the business model of healthcare continues its long- term shift away from fee-for-service to fee-for-value, CFOs are starting to shift their focus from strictly driving the top line to figuring out how to help their organizations drive the bottom line in a value-based structure.

While revenue cycle management has been the required application to invest in and deploy for the last 20 years, advanced cost accounting may be the "killer app" for the next 20 years.

And it's easy to see why. A recent survey of 100 hospital and healthcare delivery system executives conducted by Strata Decision Technology and *Becker's Healthcare*, found 90 percent of those responsible for care don't know the cost of it. This gap is driving the rapid adoption of more advanced cost accounting applications that make data more accurate, accessible and actionable.

CFOs are now recognizing this simple fatal flaw — how can you manage cost if the people responsible for it have no access to information? Recognizing that over $3.2 trillion is spent on healthcare in the U.S. every year, with over $1 trillion flowing through hospitals, the lack of tools to effectively understand and manage the cost of care represents a black hole of stunning proportions.

The end result is most CFOs are left to manage the cost crisis in the pitch dark. The typical CFO for a U.S. healthcare delivery system is managing the financial engine for a multi-billion dollar business with thousands of employees and razor-thin operating margins that average 2 percent. They are seeing their core inpatient business declining in volume by close to 3 percent per year over the last five years. With that said, their biggest challenge ahead is that their already shaky business model is being flipped upside down with the introduction of capitated and bundled payment programs that hold hospital systems accountable for taking on the risk of a fixed top line.

With margins this thin, growth this challenging and a future this uncertain, you would quickly conclude that understanding and managing cost would be mission critical.

Surprisingly, over 90 percent of U.S. hospitals either don't have a cost accounting system or have one that is outdated and insufficient. And physicians and other clinicians whose decisions control roughly 80 percent of a hospital's total spending are provided with little to no information on cost.

The end result is a lack of accurate and actionable cost data that has made consistently understanding, managing and driving out cost close to impossible.

The need to understand cost is increasing due to market pressures. Hospital systems' growing participation in capitated or risk-based payment models is driving organizations to see value in gaining a deeper understanding of their clinical data and true costs, as well as how those data sets interact. In these new models, the need to understand margin is very clear. Without accurate costing data, healthcare organizations are flying blind in these agreements and deciding how to improve processes, redesign care and drive value is extraordinarily difficult.

Recognizing the operational issues that need to be solved and the strategic value of understanding cost, hospital system CFOs are moving quickly to implement advanced cost accounting applications that provide accurate, accessible and actionable information on the cost of care delivery for their organization.

The Strata/*Becker's* survey and associated research identified three common issues in hospital cost accounting that need to be addressed:

1. Current cost accounting methods are seen as inaccurate, and the information isn't used.

2. Most hospital systems aren't able to define cost across the care continuum.

3. Most hospital systems don't trust their data.

Ensuring financial leaders use high-quality data to support clinical and strategic decision making is critical. Feeding low- quality data into analytics or using inaccurate data to drive decision making can produce the wrong conclusion and negatively affect patient care and financial performance. With that said, many hospitals still continue to run a costing process, produce data no one uses and waste time and resources.

> *Over the last five years, legacy cost accounting systems are increasingly being replaced by advanced cost accounting applications that provide accurate, accessible and actionable cost information.*

Over the last five years, legacy cost accounting systems are increasingly being replaced by advanced cost accounting applications that provide accurate, accessible and actionable cost information. Advanced cost accounting includes a set of methodologies including time-based, activity-based costing (ABC), as well as supply-based and pharmacy-based costing, cost study and relative value unit (RVU) based costing.

One methodology alone is not sufficient to consistently and accurately understand cost in healthcare. Healthcare is very different from other industries due to the data available, the variety of patient conditions, physician preferences, site of care, as well as the non-homogeneity of expenses and how they are tracked. Cost accounting needs to accurate and comprehensive, but most importantly is has to be a scalable process.

Advanced cost accounting helps address these issues. Expenses are categorized and attributed to patients based on the most practical and accurate methodology available to a provider organization. It provides a library of approaches based on the setting as well as data available to automate the process, such as EHR-based time stamps. The focus is on all the potential opportunities for identifying variation while ensuring the effort is worth the output. Leveraging a data-driven approach reduces the need for manual intervention to identify costs and enables organizations to identify true cost variation for every patient.

The Strata/*Becker's* research identified the key factors driving hospital systems to adopt advanced cost accounting solutions in preparation for value-based medicine:

1. Understanding true margins.

2. Identifying opportunities to reduce cost.

3. Viewing the total cost of care across the continuum from both inpatient and outpatient settings.

4. Sharing the financial impact of harm events and variations in clinical care.

5. Accessing accurate cost information more quickly and frequently.

6. Creating an integrated approach to financial planning and performance.

In the past, cost accounting has been undervalued and underutilized as accuracy and accessibility of information on cost wasn't seen as a necessity in traditional volume-driven payment models. This is not the case in risk- or value-based medicine. Without credible and detailed cost data, it will be extraordinarily difficult for healthcare organizations to strategically manage their operations and minimize the impact of declining reimbursement.

With close to 90 percent of healthcare leaders operating in the dark on cost, leveraging data from advanced cost accounting that is comprehensive, accurate and accessible is mission critical in helping providers collaborate and make more informed decisions, bend the cost curve, and ultimately deliver more value to the patients and the community that they serve. This is why advanced cost accounting is quickly becoming the next "killer app" for hospital CFOs.

Republished, with permission, from Becker's Hospital Review, November 21, 2017.

10 Reasons Why Hospitals are Shifting to Advanced Cost Accounting

By Dan Michelson

In light of major changes regarding reimbursement and care delivery models, cost has become mission-critical for every hospital and healthcare delivery system.

The movement from traditional revenue cycle management and managing the "top line" to a margin and outcomes management approach of improving the "bottom line" is driving the need to understand cost at a deeper and more actionable level.

Like electronic health records and population health management solutions from a clinical perspective, advanced cost accounting is now seen as an essential building block for competing in the future from a financial perspective.

As traditional cost accounting and financial decision support solutions have significant limitations, here are the top 10 reasons why hospitals are implementing more advanced cost accounting solutions.

1. To understand true margins

To effectively participate in bundled or capitated contracts, it is essential to understand true margins on an episode, service line and population basis. Traditional cost accounting systems ended at the hospital door and did not provide an outpatient view, resulting in only a partial view of cost. Organizations now require advanced cost accounting solutions that provide a full view of cost coupled with payer contract revenue modeling projections. Together, this reveals true margins and identifies where an organization may be losing money and how it can improve on an episode of care, service line or population basis.

2. To identify opportunities to reduce cost

As pressure on the top line continues to increase, most organizations have initiatives in place to reduce their cost of care delivery by eight or nine figures. They need both the data and the analytics that come with advanced cost accounting to proactively identify cost reduction opportunities by service line, facility and/or cost category, such as labor and supplies. The ability to conduct variation analysis from many different angles and then drill down into cost drivers has become an essential skill set and workflow for every organization.

3. To understand total cost of care from both inpatient and outpatient costs

There is now a need to understand cost across the entire continuum of care – not just in a hospital setting. Traditional cost accounting systems don't provide the flexibility to integrate cost data from physician practices, a central component for more advanced solutions. As care continues to shift outside the four walls of the hospital and organizations pursue a population health strategy and assume risk, the ability to get a total picture of cost has become essential.

4. To bring together financial and clinical outcomes data

All organizations are working to bring clinical data (from their EHR) and financial data (from cost accounting) together to assess and improve overall outcomes. This balanced view of performance is central to reducing variation and competing in a value-based care setting and is a major driver in the movement toward advanced cost accounting. Many organizations are now educating their physician leaders on cost and margin and are effectively presenting physician variation on a service line basis. This can't be done effectively without clinical and financial data coming together.

> *Many organizations are now educating their physician leaders on cost and margin and are effectively presenting physician variation on a service line basis.*

5. To integrate EHR, ERP and EDW

Traditional cost accounting solutions did not provide the appropriate level of integration with core EHR and enterprise resource planning systems, which is critical to bringing together clinical and financial data, but also to saving time, increasing productivity and improving accuracy. These systems also had limitations in their ability to move cost data into the enterprise data warehouse, which is now a requirement. Advanced cost accounting systems have proven integration with these systems and fit into the overall IT strategy for the organization as a source of "cost data fuel" for the overall EDW engine and strategy for the organization.

6. To integrate cost accounting with overall financial management

Traditional cost accounting solutions were standalone applications. They couldn't measure progress against cost reduction initiatives or incorporate improvements into an adjusted long-range financial plan or operating budget. The movement toward a single platform for clinical (the EHR) has caused many to take the same approach to the financial side of the house. For many, cost accounting is now part of an integrated financial management strategy that includes long-range financial planning as well as operational and capital budgeting. This allows an organization to identify a cost savings opportunity via cost accounting and then adjust their long-range financial plan and operating budget to ensure the cost savings stick.

7. To understand how to price right

Pricing transparency has become a very hot topic for every health system. But how do you set prices without knowing your costs? Do you know whether you are making or losing money? Most organizations acknowledge they are flying blind, and they are putting advanced cost accounting systems in place to address this gap.

8. To run costing quickly and more often

Hospitals and health systems have deployed an EHR and now have instant access to clinical outcomes data. However, the same access is not available for their financial data. The reliance on older, inefficient cost accounting systems has caused most organizations to run their costing process just once or twice per year. Most traditional systems take five days to run a costing process versus just five minutes with the more advanced systems on the market today. Since making cost data liquid (instantly accessible) is a key focus of most organizations, many are re-evaluating their needs and implementing new advanced cost accounting solutions.

9. To improve the accuracy of costing data

Most traditional cost accounting systems produced data that key stakeholders did not trust, and therefore, it did not get used. This was related to inflexibility and inefficiency of these systems. More advanced systems have costing engines that provide the ability to model cost using multiple methodologies (RVUs, activity-based costing, time-driven activity-based costing, supply cost, etc.). The end result is more accurate and actionable data sets for the organization.

10. To make the data more actionable via executive and operational dashboards

The ongoing frustration of many finance departments is they send out reports and no one opens them. Yet they continue to send them. Advanced cost accounting solutions incorporate advanced dashboards, data presentation and reporting tools to make data user-friendly and actionable.

Conclusion

This is a time of immense change for all stakeholders in healthcare. The question everyone is struggling with is what do I need to do now to prepare for where we are heading?

As we shift to a system of care that is more focused on outcomes, it has become very clear there will continue to be a movement away from strictly a "top line" focus toward the "bottom line," from a clinical and financial outcomes perspective. In that light, understanding cost and true margins has moved from a "nice to have" to a "need to have." And with that movement, advanced cost accounting has become an essential competency for every healthcare delivery system.

Republished, with permission, from Becker's Hospital Review, April 1, 2014.

2.3

The Four Biggest Cost Accounting Mistakes You Don't Know You're Making

CREATE A NEW MINDSET, SKILLSET AND TOOLSET

By Tushar Pandey

If healthcare providers share a common priority, it is cost reduction.

A recent HIMSS survey bears this out, with cost reduction cited as the highest priority among U.S. healthcare systems. That's no surprise, given the rapid emergence of fee-for-value payment models. These models require management not only of service line margins, but patient outcomes as well. However, the industry is just beginning to appreciate the enormity of the task.

Advanced cost accounting is not just a new process or strategy, but rather entails what many providers consider to be an entirely new mindset around the relationship between clinical performance and financial performance. Advanced cost accounting software and systems can help – indeed are a must – but without new ways of thinking, the effort to contain cost can easily flounder.

Here are four common mistakes I have encountered during my work implementing cost accounting systems with more than 200 healthcare delivery organizations. These are not the kind of inadvertent mistakes we all make, such as forgetting to attach a document to an e-mail. Rather, they more broadly reflect the ingrained work habits of the fee-for-service era and the corresponding management and systems structure that often supported it. I offer this list in hopes of stimulating new thinking around one overarching goal: better understanding and managing cost.

Mistake #1: Cost data is not accurate

During a recent webcast on this topic, I polled the audience as to which of eight common costing methodologies they were using. Not surprisingly, several of the methods – such as RVU-based accounting and ratio of cost to charge – are among the preferred tools. Some of the 600 providers in the audience were even using such time-consuming methods, such as time-driven activity-based costing.

Here's the bad news: each of these methods can be useful on its own for limited purposes, but sophisticated cost accounting cannot rest solely on one methodology. Effective cost accounting must be a mix of all different methodologies depending on the situation and availability of data. For instance, costing of supplies using RVU or RCC will only provide an average cost and will be inadequate to understand variation as it relates to choices made per patient. Instead a patient-level markup or patient-level cost data must be leveraged.

When performed correctly, cost accounting can shed more light on a payer contract offering say, a slight premium above the Medicare rate for a certain procedure. What at first glance appears to be a profitable contract becomes more dubious as additional information is added to the analysis. The ability to negotiate more favorable payer contracts is just one benefit of avoiding this all too common mistake.

Mistake #2: Cost data is too limited in scope

Health systems invariably focus on hospital costs, often ignoring what is happening in their physician clinics, home health agencies and ancillary settings. It's an incomplete picture at best, and a misleading one at worst. In the era of bundled payments, tracking a patient's entire cost of care across the spectrum of the hospital departments and professional service settings will be obligatory. Service line profitability will become a measure not only for the local hospital department, but of the direct and indirect costs associated with professional services as well. Enterprise profitability across the health system, now understood in only the most generic terms, will be revealed in far greater detail. If you avoid this mistake, and broaden your financial perspective, your analytical capabilities grow in tandem. Comparing cost per case among physicians, for example, or understanding the labor requirements for a given population of patients, is now possible.

Mistake #3: Cost data is inaccessible

Here is my mantra when it comes to sharing cost data: Cost data is only as meaningful as the number of people with access to it. In many legacy cost accounting systems, getting access to cost reports often entails:

1. Putting in a request to IT to run a report

2. Waiting days for the report

3. Figuring out that the delivered report should have included another variable

4. Returning to step one

Advanced cost accounting creates an infrastructure that enables self-service for financial analysts, department leaders and physician executives alike. At some delivery systems, such as Fairview Health Services, based in Minneapolis, this approach is blossoming. In stark contrast to its legacy approach, Fairview now grants more than 150 analysts immediate, 24/7 access to its cost accounting system. It blends data from the EHR, general ledger, physician practice management and enterprise resource planning systems. Before Fairview revamped its approach to cost accounting, the health system had only two data administrators with direct access and report writing capability.

The expansion of the user community – a move predicated on a robust training and education requirement on how to use the data – has helped reinforce the idea that cost accountability is everyone's business. Give people data and their ability to identify ways to manage costs flourishes.

Mistake #4: Cost data is not actionable

Probably the biggest impediment to cost reduction is cultural. While most health systems have cost reduction projects underway, only a minority of them actually hit their target. A Strata Decision survey found that 88 percent of organizations have cost reduction targets but only 17 percent are meeting those goals. Our survey also revealed that difficulties in tracking savings, in managing projects and establishing accountability often figure.

To counter that, I encourage promotion of "data discovery," namely enabling department leaders to write their own reports, conduct their own analyses, work with their own medical staffs and create transparency around their own performance. Cost accounting need not be the domain of cost accounting "experts."

Making data actionable, however, requires far more than merely having a sophisticated tool set that integrates data from multiple sources. It all but demands new skills – skills such as adopting the sometimes arcane vocabulary of health finance. A new mind set is also called for. This means the willingness to adjust staffing levels to patient volumes, streamline management decision making and address high-cost (and unnecessary) variations in care.

If you trust your end-users and give them the right education, support and tools, their ability to tackle these tasks might surprise you.

Republished, with permission, from Becker's Hospital Review, April 20, 2015.

2.4

Finding the True
Cost of Care

By Helen Adamopoulous

Name _____
Address _____ Date _____

R̸x

IMPLEMENT
ACTIVITY-BASED
COSTING TO
PINPOINT COST
SAVINGS

MD _____
Signature _____

About two years ago, leaders at Children's Healthcare of Atlanta (CHOA) began to wonder if they could connect the facility's overhead costs to actual activity involved in treating the patient. That led to the launch of an organizational initiative that's changing how the hospital looks at the cost of providing care.

"The goal is to take overhead and move it into the direct [spending] as much as possible," says Mike Riley, CHOA's director of performance analytics.

The method CHOA is using is called activity-based costing – a way to determine the cost of a service or product based on the resources consumed. According to *The Economist*, ABC is seen as a way "to change the way in which costs are counted" and provides an alternative to traditional accounting, which involves allocating overhead or indirect costs in proportion to an activity's direct costs. The traditional method can prove problematic, as it doesn't reflect the true cost difference between services that require the same amount of direct costs but vary in their overhead (for instance, two products may require the same amount of workers and materials, but one may be more complex and take more of employees' time).

> *For hospitals and health systems facing pressure to become more efficient and contain spending, this costing methodology can provide a pathway for finding the real cost of healthcare services and utilization.*

For hospitals and health systems facing pressure to become more efficient and contain spending, this costing methodology can provide a pathway for finding the real cost of healthcare services and utilization. So far, CHOA has applied activity-based costing to areas including environmental services (e.g., room cleaning for inpatients and outpatients based on clinical care area), diabetes education, patient access and medical records maintenance. The ABC method has helped the hospital realize that historically costs weren't accounted for appropriately according to utilization, Mr. Riley says.

For hospitals and health systems looking to start using ABC, Mr. Riley identified administrative costs as "easy wins." CHOA has re-categorized administrative departments and functions to tie their costs back to care delivery. For instance, he cites the emergency department patient access cost category. "It was easy to re-class those dollars into the ED," he says. "When we re-class them, those costs were spread based on the RVUs. Regardless if it's a level-one or a level-five patient, the same work is being done by that access staff. So we were able to say we're going to spread this cost evenly per patient."

Brad Webb, manager of cost analytics at CHOA, says it helps to have the support of hospital managers when adopting ABC. "They were excited about it," he says of CHOA's leaders. Additionally, he says communicating with departments and employees affected by the shift is crucial so that they understand what's happening.

Mr. Riley advises working with the department leads in areas where the hospital plans to move from an overhead to a direct cost component. "Make sure you understand how their services are delivered and what services you provide…so that when you start down this process you don't realize it's not what you thought it was," he says. "In a large organization…they might just look at the description on the cost center and decide how to spread overhead. That description of that department in the accounting system doesn't always match what they're doing on the ground."

CHOA has made a lot of progress with the new costing method, but it's only 50 to 60 percent done with its journey, according to Mr. Riley. "The last 40 percent is going to take longer," he says. "To get the operational buy-in on some of this is just going to take time." However, Mr. Riley and his colleagues are prepared to put in the effort.

"We're starting to have conversations on what are the next three departments we want to address," he says. "We're going to continue to push forward and push the envelope for the foreseeable future."

Republished, with permission, from Becker's Hospital Review, August 26, 2014.

2.5

Using Dashboards to Drive Better Performance

By Laura Ramos Hegwer

The decision support team at Baptist Health, Little Rock, Ark., has implemented a new process combined with a self-service reporting tool to help service line leaders monitor their financial performance—and make quick decisions when needed.

"Our organization looks at our service line managers as catalysts for change," says Brock Holman, director of managed care and decision support for Baptist Health, which is Arkansas' largest not-for-profit healthcare delivery network. "We believe we should arm them with data and allow them to be responsible for their performance."

At the same time, providing service line leaders with the ability to access self-service dashboards frees the decision support team to work on broader, system wide initiatives, such as population health management. Baptist Health has one system-level CFO, but there are no hospital-level CFOs or dedicated financial analysts. The organization's seven-member decision support team is responsible for operational accounting, labor management, contract management, forecasting, cost accounting, decision support, and ad hoc financial reporting.

"We have adopted a self-service approach to dashboards because of the scope of the work that we do and the limited number of analysts that we have in the organization," Holman says. "We had to develop tools that users could drive themselves."

A self-service model

Up until last year, dashboard reporting was a mostly manual process that Holman's team managed on an ad hoc basis. Before they adopted a new decision support platform, they had relied on a homegrown system using Structured Query Language (SQL) that pulled data from their electronic health record. A basic business intelligence tool only allowed analysts to develop "flat" reports that did not allow for much detail or customization. As a result, analysts spent a lot of time fielding and responding to new report requests each time a new need arose.

Baptist Health saved an estimated $200,000 a year from just one change driven by its new dashboards.

Turnaround time was another issue, says Andrew Covington, manager of decision support. "The bottleneck would sometimes be on us because we had to prioritize what we could do," he says. At the same time, the decision support team was reluctant to say no to leaders who were engaged in critical performance improvement efforts.

Fortunately, the addition of self-reporting capabilities has created more capacity for Holman's team to take on more work. Now users can access self-service dashboards for service line, profitability, and utilization reporting.

Service line dashboards

One example is the development of the "charge-based" service line report that the decision support team created for its newest hospital in Conway, Ark. The team needed a way to monitor volumes without having to wait for patients to be discharged/coded. "We developed service-line logic that groups patients based on the charges that have posted to their accounts, regardless of discharge/coded status," Covington says. "It provides the service line leaders with more timely data, so they do not have to wait until the end of the month."

Profitability dashboards

The decision support team also has developed summary and detailed profitability dashboards that service line leaders can use to identify potential opportunities for the revenue cycle, cost savings, and costing methodology refinement.

For example, incorrectly coded charges in the revenue cycle can present substantial opportunities. Leaders used the tool to identify why some outpatient procedures had both a net loss and a negative direct margin. They determined that some implants were being incorrectly charged as non-implants, resulting in missed implant-specific payment. "There was a disconnect between the service line people and the revenue cycle people," Covington says.

The profitability dashboards are used to identify trends in the following areas.

Payer mix. Service line leaders also can use the reports to identify payer mix and collection issues that can affect the revenue cycle, such as denials. When reviewing the neurosurgery service line, the team identified three cases for which the hospital received no payments because they were denied by Medicare. They also found some instances in which the hospital was repeatedly missing a charge for inpatient obstetrics cases. "We were missing out on reimbursement because of that," Holman says.

Utilization. Regarding cost savings opportunities, service line leaders can use the profitability reports to identify physician variation in utilization, as well as length of stay and contract negotiation issues.

RVUs. In terms of costing methodology, service line leaders can use the reports to help identify opportunities to update RVUs. They also might find accounting issues that can create erroneous results. For example, revenue and/or expenses posting to the incorrect cost center, resulting in a disconnected relationship.

Utilization dashboards

The decision support team also developed utilization dashboards that can assist leaders in identifying differences between facilities and physicians when similar services are performed.

For example, users can focus on inpatient medical supplies to identify opportunities to standardize costs and increase margins. Specifically, they can identify average supply cost per physician by DRG and identify variation.

For example, when reviewing the utilization of spinal implants, the neurosurgery service line leader met with physicians to discuss the data. The physicians were receptive and identified at least one opportunity to reduce variation in supply use. In fact, they were surprised to learn that one item cost twice as much as another and agreed to standardize to the less expensive item. As a result of this one change, they will save an estimated $200,000 a year.

Lessons learned

Before rolling out the tool to the entire organization, Holman and Covington tested the new reporting process with a small user group. Today, hundreds of users across the organization utilize the decision support tool to access self-service dashboards.

Covington and Holman offer the following advice for CFOs and other finance leaders who want to leverage dashboards to improve organizational performance.

Market the initiative across the organization. "The CFO needs to sell the process and tell the organization that they have to transition to a new way of getting information and having conversations," Holman says.

Give the decision support team and vendor adequate time to roll out the tool properly. "The CFO needs to be able to provide the resources to support this type of implementation and allow some other responsibilities to be put on hold," Holman says.

With an advanced cost accounting tool, we can make better strategy decisions.

Ensure clean data from day one. "Data issues can be the biggest holdup in a process like this," Covington says. "Be skeptical about any data element you have and test it for completeness and reasonableness."

Holman agrees. "No one expects the data to be perfect," he says. "But it will kill a conversation [with an operational leader] if you can't stand behind the data. We can have tools but credibility is really our best asset."

Train service line managers on using the new tool. Although leaders at Baptist Health have not rolled out a formal training curriculum on the decision support tool for service line managers, Covington provides one-on-one training or group presentations on the tool. "We target people who we know are engaged," he says.

Let service line leaders set the agenda for improving performance. "Our organization is large but not so large that we do not know the physicians who are likely to drive change," Holman says. "If we find something in the reports, we will ask [service line leaders] about it. But we want these activities to be operations driven, not finance driven. It's a better conversation whenever operations drives this."

Looking ahead to episodic performance

Holman says his decision support team is working with key leaders in Baptist Health's physician organization to determine how they are going to approach episodic-based performance down the road, such as through a cardiac bundle. One of their goals is to build the functionality across the organization that will be needed to help leaders monitor their clinical and financial indicators.

"Our concern is that if you can't marry up your claims data with your cost data, you may never be able to drive the kind of change that you need to," Holman says. "[With the decision support tool,] we can make better strategy decisions."

2.6

Leveraging Decision Support for Costing and Planning

By Laura Ramos Hegwer

Two years ago, finance leaders at Augusta University Health System were eager to make their decision support processes more efficient and powerful. This was critical as the Augusta, Ga. based organization was undergoing a transformation, including a name change (the health system was formerly known as Georgia Regents Health) and planning for a future expansion. Currently, the health system includes Georgia's only public academic medical center, a children's hospital, and more than 80 outpatient practices. Augusta University Health System also holds a certificate of need (CON) to build a 100-bed hospital in an adjacent county.

Such large-scale change required leaders to lean on their data so they could confidently plan for the future. But that confidence was lacking, as reports crunched by different teams sometimes revealed different data.

"When I came to Augusta two years ago, financial planning and analysis, including decision support, was broken into silos, and people did not realize they often were replicating the same reports," says Suzanne Wojtowicz, director, financial planning and analysis. Her goal was to create an agile analytics team and implement a platform so leaders across the organization would have access to the same information.

Tackling perioperative costs

After hiring analytics expertise and piloting a renovation and expansion of the decision support system, Wojtowicz recognized the need to prioritize her team's efforts by areas with the greatest opportunity. One early focus area was perioperative services, which included the adult operating room, the children's hospital operating room, labor and delivery, the cardiac catheterization lab, and the digestive health center. These service lines shared the same IT platform and would require the same types of interfaces with the new decision support system.

Michael Phipps, business manager of perioperative services, had a specific goal at the outset: to calculate the true cost of a case so he could develop meaningful case cost reports. Specifically, he wanted other leaders to understand how variation between physicians affected costs. He also wanted to link costs to clinical outcomes, such as surgical-site infections and blood loss.

In addition, Phipps wanted to create more sophisticated block-utilization reports to determine which surgical procedures created ROI for the institution. "In most institutions, the most valuable real estate is your surgical OR," he says.

Phipps worked with Wojtowicz to identify the most accurate data source and integrate case cost data with financial data in the health system's new decision support system. As a result of their efforts, the organization now can directly attribute equipment costs to specific procedure codes and cases, such as robot-assisted surgeries. In the past, $10 million in equipment and labor costs associated with these cases was distributed among all OR cases, clouding the true costs.

Increasing physician confidence in the data was another key goal. With the new reports, leaders have a much clearer picture of the true cost of a case. From there, they can work with surgeons to discuss ways to standardize care and reduce costs. "Most surgeons are very competitive with each other, and they will look to drive down the cost of each individual case and standardize the set of supplies that go with it," Phipps says. For example, the perioperative services department recently completed a standardization effort around endomechanical devices. By moving from multiple vendors to a single vendor, leaders saved $220,000 in the first six months of the current fiscal year. They also are consolidating the use of biosurgery (hemostatis) products, which is expected to save $230,000 annually across the perioperative services and pharmacy departments.

Case Cost Reporting: Augusta University Health System

By better understanding average costs per case, leaders can engage surgeons in discussions about variation and standardization strategies.

Provider	Procedure	Preference Card Cost 1/27/16	Average Cost/Case
Dr. A	Resection colon laparoscopic	$536.68	$2, 666.86
Dr. B	Resection colon laparoscopic	$654.71	$3,305.04
Dr. C	Resection colon laparoscopic	$702.38	$1,655.18

Provider	Procedure	Case Number	Actual Cost
Dr. A	Resection colon laparoscopic	MAIN-2015-11806	$2,430.36
		MAIN-2015-12550	$2,921.69
		MAIN-2015-17120	$2,648.53
			$2,666.86 average cost/ provider
Dr. B	Resection colon laparoscopic	MAIN-2015-6891	$3,283.59
		MAIN-2015-14238	$3,421.01
		MAIN-2015-8641	$3,210.53
			$3,305.04 average cost/ provider
Dr. C	Resection colon laparoscopic	MAIN-2015-15060	$1,588.55
		MAIN-2015-15817	$1,644.08
		MAIN-2015-12848	$1,732.92
			$1,655.18 average cost/ provider

Source: Augusta University Health System and Strata Decision Technology. Used with permission.

Published in HFMA's *Healthcare Cost Containment*, February 2017 (hfma.org/hcc).

Grounding decisions in data

In addition to their cost reduction efforts, leaders at Augusta University Health System were consumed with planning the new 100-bed hospital. Specifically, they needed to calculate space needs based on clinical growth projections. "It can be just as dangerous to under-build as it is to overbuild," says Jennifer Smith, assistant vice president of planning design and construction.

Smith and her colleagues wanted to predict how adding services at the new hospital might affect volumes at the flagship hospital and other locations. "I wanted to be able to look across a single encounter in a particular service and see the effect on ancillary services," Smith says. "But there wasn't one single place I could go to for that information in all of our systems." When Wojtowicz learned of Smith's struggles, she suggested using the same decision support platform to help with facilities planning.

Now, Wojtowicz and Smith meet weekly with a newly formed business development team, which includes the health system CFO, the vice president of facilities, and directors from marketing and outreach. During these meetings, the team leverages market share, volume projections, and other data for long-term planning purposes. They also share robust inpatient and outpatient volume forecasts with a third party that specializes in long-range planning. From there, leaders can determine whether to accept or reject a business proposal.

Access to this data also has helped leaders have more informed discussions when recruiting talent from other organizations. They have projections based on reality, rather than optimism, Smith says.

In fact, Smith wants all of the health system's strategic planning decisions to be grounded in reliable data. To that end, she uses the reports to help her determine when it is time to respectfully push back and ask a department leader for more information to back up his projections.

Smith also uses reports to develop the facilities master plan and determine capital needs. "We're really looking forward to tying the capital planning with the strategic planning," she says.

Sharing lessons learned

Leaders at Augusta University Health System offer the following advice for other finance leaders looking to reinvent decision support at their organizations.

The health system can now report pharmacy costs per case and by service line, including inpatient versus outpatient costs.

Empower your team members to become subject matter experts. Wojtowicz asked her team to "specialize" in specific areas of decision support so they can be resources to others in the organization.

Check your interfaces between systems. These are essential to making sure costs are being accurately transmitted from the materials system into your costing systems, Phipps says. He created the position of inventory control coordinator to monitor these interfaces and validate costs.

Standardize service definitions in every reporting system. Now that service definitions are the same organization wide, planning exercises are more accurate and meaningful.

Use decision support to understand pharmacy costs. Leaders at Augusta University Health System engaged a consultant to help them develop a tool to arrive at accurate costs that reflect group purchasing organization versus 340B pricing, as well as map costs by patient location and labor category. As a result, the health system can now report pharmacy costs per case and by service line, including inpatient versus outpatient costs.

Bringing transparency to the entire organization

Today, financial planning and analysis at Augusta University Health System is no longer siloed and inefficient, thanks to better coordination and tools.

To reduce ad hoc reporting requests, Wojtowicz and her team have created dashboards for specific audiences, including leaders in the C-suite, perioperative services, ancillary services, ambulatory services, and revenue cycle.

However, she warns against the dangers of overwhelming leaders with too much data. "You have to be mindful of the audience for each of these reports and keep the reports manageable," she says.

Digging deep for cost data

By integrating case cost data with financial data in its decision support system, Augusta University Health System can now gain a clear picture of the true cost of a single patient case. This big picture view also helps leaders better leverage data on market share and volume projections for long-term planning purposes.

Republished, with permission, from the February 2017 issue of Healthcare Cost Containment.
Copyright 2017, Healthcare Finance Management Association.
Three Westbrook Corporate Center, Suite 600, Westchester, IL 60154-5732.
For more information, call 800-252-HFMA or vist hfma.org.

PART THREE

Best Practices in Bending
the Cost Curve

Overview

By Dan Michelson

When discussing his marketing budget, John Wanamaker, an early 20th Century retailer, reportedly said, "Half my advertising is wasted. I just don't know which half." Healthcare providers charged with implementing cost reductions would surely empathize with Wanamaker's dilemma. It's become a working industry assumption that many of our healthcare dollars are wasted – due to unnecessary treatments, over-utilization of tests and duplication services. Inefficiency prevails. The Institute of Medicine claims the annual waste tab is nearly $765 billion, a staggering number approaching nearly 30 percent of outlays.

But finding the waste and taking it out turns out to be easier said than done. Successful efforts in reducing cost are few and far between. According to a recent study by Strata Decision Technology, 88 percent of providers have cost savings initiatives underway, yet only 17 percent are hitting the target. Physicians, whose decisions control roughly 80 percent of the spend in healthcare, are constantly feeling pressure to reduce cost yet few have been provided the data they need to make that happen. But if you don't know how much something costs, how can you be expected to find ways to reduce the cost?

In this section a number of industry experts discuss how to break through the wall to drive out cost in a sustainable way. The principles we will explore – a combination of technology, management and training – provide a path to bend the cost curve and drive margin for healthcare providers in all settings of care. Technology alone is not enough. Without a thoughtful management approach – one driven from the top of the organization – any effort in reducing cost will likely fizzle. A successful cost reduction effort can involve everybody – from front-end scheduling to back-end accounts receivable management to front line managers who are now using data analytics to keep staffing levels in line with volume and service line mix.

Managing cost reduction in today's healthcare delivery system requires abandoning old ways of thinking. Successful efforts require changing the culture by offering the right technology to do the job, training staff to use the tools and adopting an effective leadership approach. Flipping the cost crisis into an opportunity requires open sourcing solutions. Our goal is to get that conversation started.

Stories in this section detail the building blocks that must be put in place to help bend the cost curve, including:

3.1

Establishing a Successful Cost Reduction Program

By Liz Kirk

MAKE COST MANAGEMENT CONTINUOUS, NOT EPISODIC

In an era of mounting fiscal uncertainty marked by flat, even downward trending net revenue lines, the need for reducing cost has never been greater. Yet, many cost reduction strategies fall flat: operational benchmarking, lean, clinical pathways, minimizing variation, flexing to volume, hiring expensive consultants…the list goes on.

In the end, most providers say that these initiatives either did not produce the level of savings needed or that the cost crept back into the organization. With unprecedented top line pressure, this time, it is absolutely imperative that providers find cost savings opportunities, implement them effectively, and hold the gain over the long term.

There are two principles that are foundational to a successful cost improvement program: 1) operating expense actually has to come out; 2) the organization has to have strong systems and structures in place to identify, quantify, execute and sustain cost savings. In other words, provider organizations don't need a one-time cost reduction initiative; they need a continuous cost improvement program.

It all starts with two key principles:

Principle #1: Operating expense actually has to come out

It's unfortunate, but true, that healthcare providers spend a lot of time and energy working to "improve efficiency" or "reduce the cost of care" – neither of which actually result in any real, measurable cost savings that can be seen in financial statements. Aside from growing the top line, reducing operating expenses is the only way to improve the bottom line. That means expense must come out – fewer FTEs, fewer supplies ordered, lower acquisition costs for implants, less money spent on contracted services, or reduced outlays for staff benefits. Reducing utilization of services provided will reduce the charges on a patient's bill, and reimbursement in some cases, but organizations will only experience any real cost savings if they also reduce corresponding staff and supply expenses that correspond to that volume.

When the senior leaders responsible for cost savings initiatives do not hold teams accountable to these standards, the result is often "soft dollar savings," namely gains in efficiency that do not result in a reduction of expenses. A common example is reducing length of stay (LOS). Unless the improvement reduces the number of hours worked or allows another inpatient case to fill the bed, there is no impact to financial performance.

Principle #2: Strong systems and structures must be focused on cost improvement

Regardless of the methodology used to identify cost savings opportunities, having a strong central leadership model constitutes the primary differentiator between successful cost improvement programs and ineffective initiatives.

On the rare occasion that cost savings efforts do not fail with a lack of strong leadership and structures, they will generally only realize some savings and not the entire intended savings targets. Strong central leadership helps not only to unite the organization around shared goals, but also to continuously manage and track progress against those set goals. Leaders must also ensure that teams within the cost improvement program are strategically positioned for success by equipping them with the proper knowledge, tools and skills to actually drive out cost.

With those principles in place there are five key elements required to establish and manage a successful and ongoing cost improvement program:

Key element #1: Strong, collaborative leadership

Driving cost out cannot be a siloed endeavor. Senior leadership for the cost improvement initiative must be a collaboration between operations, finance and clinical leaders. The group of executive sponsors ideally should encompass the Chief Operations Officer (COO), Chief Financial Officer (CFO), Chief Nursing Officer (CNO) and Chief Medical Officer (CMO). All other senior leaders should be accountable for achieving their respective division's cost savings goals and enabling the achievement of the entire organizational goal.

The main role of senior leadership is to provide guidance and boundaries to cost improvement teams, to push them to innovate and re-think how care is provided, to hold teams and owners accountable for achieving goals, and to communicate a clear, consistent message to all stakeholders.

Key element #2: Thoughtful guiding principles

Leadership sets the tone for the cost improvement initiative and is ultimately responsible for engaging operational, clinical and administrative leaders in the process. It's a delicate enterprise: clinical and operational leaders may feel threatened by cost reduction initiatives. They fear that reductions will jeopardize patient satisfaction or quality. However, cost savings can be realized simultaneously to and by means of fixing broken processes, strengthening management skills and boosting quality. But, without leadership explicitly stating and restating this idea, it is nearly impossible for the organization to take this positive perspective when looking for savings opportunities.

Ask yourself, "What CAN we do with $300M?" not "What do we have to GIVE UP to cut $40M?"

- Maintain or improve quality and patient satisfaction

- Minimize impact to front line staff

- Improve the operations of organization, especially patient throughput

- Increase the ability for managers to impact outcomes

- Strengthen management skills

- Strive for highest and best use of individual staff

- Think big, but be able to operationalize in 3-6 months

Key element #3: Well-defined metrics, goals and targets

Before developing a cost improvement program, providers not only need to clearly understand their cost reduction goals, but also communicate their goals in a way that compels action, not fear or hopelessness. Typically, each year, finance models the forecasted changes in volume, reimbursement rates, inflation, and the expense base needed to generate an acceptable margin. In today's environment, this usually results in a need for reduced expenses – "a budget gap of 4 percent" or "$40M reduction in cost." The same cycle repeats each year.

While this language and approach works for finance, it is confusing

Setting Goals

Continuous Cost Management (YTD vs Target in $M)

to people outside of finance because it doesn't translate to anything tangible or realistic. Also, as volume, reimbursement and patient mix change from year to year, the overall cost reduction target may change from one year to the next, which can spawn distrust between operations and finance. Moreover, identifying ways to save $40M is daunting, while identifying ways to reduce cost per case by $50 is doable.

Consider creating a cost reduction path that spans up to five years and is based on a metric that is tangible, such as cost per case mix index (CMI), adjusted equivalent admission or cost per inpatient case. The metric should account for changes in the environment and population to allow for flexibility in the overall reduction needed each year. Taking this approach will facilitate the communication of cost savings goals to front-line staff and provide clarity on what levers the organization can pull to achieve cost targets. It will also help to diminish fear among front-line staff who may equate cost savings opportunities with job loss.

Tracking Performance

Key element #4: Highly effective teams

Once a metric is selected and targets are set, it's time to charter teams and get to work. However, it is easy to move too quickly through this step and then not see results.

Teams should be created that align directly with the overall metric that is to be impacted. If the team is successful, it will positively and measurably impact the performance of the overall metric. Teams should be given targets to aim for. Focusing on these targets will push the teams to think beyond today and deliver innovative ideas. Additionally, the sum of the teams' targets should equate to more than the overall target. This over-abundance of cost savings opportunities will give the leadership team much-needed leeway to not move forward on all opportunities identified if the circumstances are not ideal.

Each team should consist of managers and directors from a cross section of the organization with expertise in different areas. Teams should be given free rein to evaluate all areas within their scope. Each team should have one or two project managers who are responsible for facilitating team meetings, obtaining and analyzing data to quantify cost savings opportunities, reporting out to senior leadership, and driving implementation. Each team should include one or two vice presidents as well. They should help identify cost reduction opportunities, but more importantly promote openness to new ideas, cross-departmental thinking, and an expectation of driving improvement, not simply cost savings. Ultimately, these senior leaders are accountable for the team's results.

Key element #5: Diligent program management

The final and perhaps most important step, is most often overlooked. In order for the savings to stick, it is critical to establish a central oversight structure that keeps the organization moving quickly and methodically. All too often, once teams are chartered, they are off and running but at different paces, with different ideas of how to take action and with a different understanding of their end goal. Adding a structured process will prevent this inefficient and ineffective use of resources.

Clearly articulating what is expected from teams at what time intervals is important to getting results at the end of the process – the more precise the instructions the better. Organizations should require that each team find $XX in saving opportunities, take the time to validate the opportunity with the impacted department, and develop a high level plan for operationalizing the change by a certain date. They should then have teams show savings in FTE reductions at the cost center and job code level or expense reductions at the GL code level. Such a deliverable-driven undertaking is very different from charging teams with a vague mission like "find and implement cost savings opportunities."

Getting to this level of detail is the only way to ensure that savings are real and can be measured on an on-going basis.

Once cost savings opportunities are finalized, adding the projected savings to the budget is the easiest way to drive accountability for sustaining results. If leaders later find they are operating with a negative budget variance, they should explain the causes and present a plan for getting back to budget.

Moreover, organizations need to have structures in place to review and approve additional expenses, such as requests for new FTEs, which may occur outside of budget season. Senior leadership councils should be established to review requests for new FTEs, replacement or temporary FTEs, consulting and new equipment. These groups should have a thoughtful, data-driven process in place to balance the need for cost savings with quality, patient satisfaction, employee engagement and physician satisfaction.

Conclusion

Cost reduction is not an easy task. Focused leadership, clear expectations and a well-orchestrated program are core to finding and delivering cost savings. Beyond that, framing "the need to reduce cost" as "an opportunity to improve our organization" is a transformative nuance. It frees team members to innovate, to address persistent problems and ultimately find better, more cost efficient ways of caring for patients. At that point, they are no longer driving out cost, but eliminating waste and inefficiency in order to drive margin to fuel your mission. Implementing a cost savings program is very different than putting a one-time cost savings initiative in place. Given the level of cost savings that is needed in most organizations and the lack of results from previous attempts, employing a centrally managed, rigorous approach is not just necessary, it is vital.

3.2

Common Mistakes in Leading Cost Reduction Initiatives

By Liz Kirk

AVOID COMMON MISTAKES IN DRIVING OUT COST

$40 million, $100 million, $220 million, $300 million. These figures do not represent recent Powerball jackpots or the contracts of star athletes. They are the annual cost reduction targets that CFOs of major health systems have recently shared with me.

Unfortunately, all too often internal cost reduction initiatives fail to produce the level of savings required. For many organizations that fall short, the next step is to call a consultant – a costly approach as the expertise and often the ownership is outsourced. While many factors may limit the effectiveness of an internal or external approach, the lack of an effective leadership structure to drive the cost reduction initiative is usually the most toxic.

To generate high levels of cost savings, providers must drill deep into operations, challenge convention, design new care models, build new organizational structures and define new roles that will continue to produce high-quality care, but at much lower cost. Clearly, driving this level of change is not for the faint of heart and strong leadership is essential – but all too often absent.

In order to get to the right leadership structure to drive cost reduction in your organization it is critical to know what doesn't work. The common mistakes in leadership structure that can limit the effectiveness of driving a major cost reduction fall into the following four areas:

1. Led by the CFO and finance

Since the need for cost savings is a financial problem, finance should lead it, right? Wrong. Typically, most finance teams are not positioned in the organization nor experienced in working side by side with clinical and operational departments to identify and implement opportunities for cost reduction.

2. Led by the COO and operational leaders

Since the need for cost savings originates in the clinical and operational departments, the leaders of these departments should lead the charge. Finance will help with calculating the savings and tracking the ongoing benefit. Sound good? Not so fast. Teams of operational and clinical leaders often focus on improving efficiency, which does not necessarily equate to cost savings. Take, for example, working to reduce turnaround time between operating room cases. Unless another case is added or worked hours are reduced, there really is no financial impact.

3. Led by everybody (essentially led by nobody)

This usually comes in the form of across the board cuts for which individual divisions or vice presidents are accountable for stepping up and hitting. The typical outcome of this approach is that so-called improvements to reduce costs ultimately sub-optimize how patients flow through the system, resulting in unexpected bottlenecks, angry patients, or worse. This leadership approach often also attempts to engage employees in the effort by asking them for ideas on where to reduce cost. While this can produce thousands of ideas, the ability of a health system to vet, validate, coordinate and implement all of these ideas is virtually impossible and the ROI is often minimal.

4. Led by performance improvement (PI) teams

Hospitals that have PI teams are a fortunate bunch. However, all too often, these change agents are assigned to projects that have a relatively limited scope and only address a piece of a much larger problem. When the PI team is not coordinated to drive toward a single key metric – in this case, cost – their work often doesn't deliver the level of savings required.

Now, you may be thinking that there is no effective model for leading major cost reduction initiatives, since I just dismissed what everyone in the industry is doing right now. And this is exactly the message here – doing more of the same will only get us more of the same, which isn't working.

Here is the best leadership approach for a successful cost reduction initiative:

- A partnership between the CFO and COO with a commitment to hit the savings targets while maintaining or improving quality and patient satisfaction.

- Engaged and accountable senior leaders who will push cross-functional teams to think deeply about the status quo and to develop innovative approaches to doing more with less.

- Support teams, such as HR, IT and clinical leaders, who are poised to act on the recommendations of the teams and make those cost savings happen.

- One or more dedicated, influential "cost leaders" who establish targets and time lines, organize teams, partner with finance and operations to identify and implement measurable improvements, and are accountable to senior leadership.

No matter where you may be on your cost reduction journey, now is the time to stop and think. Are you set up to achieve goals and meet targets? Are you set up to fall short like the others that came before you? Will you be making an expensive phone call to a consultant?

Many have reached the conclusion that this time cost reduction is not an initiative, but rather something that will need to be a core competency for every healthcare delivery system. Putting the right leadership structure in place will lead to you more effectively bending the cost curve, both right now and further down the road.

Republished, with permission, from Healthcare Finance News, April 18, 2014.

3.3

Health Systems See Money Saving Efforts Fail Before They Even Start

By Ayla Ellison

As the healthcare industry migrates toward a value-based payment system, with risk-based models like bundled payments gaining speed, it is vital for hospitals and health systems to reduce costs. However, that process is difficult when organizations don't know their costs.

During an executive roundtable discussion at the *Becker's Hospital Review* 7th Annual Meeting in Chicago, Dan Michelson, CEO of Strata Decision Technology, said the confusion around "cost" begins with the definition. When hospital leaders discuss costs, some refer to price, while others refer to charges or reimbursement. "When you get in a room, the most important thing is to make sure everyone is using the same definition," said Mr. Michelson.

After arriving at a common definition, organizations need to ensure the cost information they're relying on is accurate. Obtaining correct cost information is often a difficult task in the healthcare industry. To emphasize this, Mr. Michelson shared a quote from a 2013 Harvard Business Review article written by Michael Porter, PhD, an economist and professor at Harvard Business School. "The absence of accurate cost information in healthcare is nothing short of astounding," wrote Dr. Porter. "Healthcare organizations are flying blind in deciding how to improve processes and redesign care."

Dr. Porter's insight is especially astute given the focus on cost reduction in the industry. Mr. Michelson said cost reduction has moved to the top of many organizations' priorities. He referenced a survey of 100 healthcare CFOs and vice presidents of finance that revealed nine out of 10 had a cost savings initiative in place at their organization. However, many organizations aren't satisfied with their progress — 88 percent said their cost saving efforts fell short.

Advanced cost accounting can address many shortcomings in organizations' current cost savings initiatives.

Advanced cost accounting can address many shortcomings in organizations' current cost savings initiatives. "This is where the market is going," said Mr. Michelson. An advanced cost accounting system offers organizations a complete picture, including accurate information on both inpatient and outpatient costs. This type of system relies on relative value units (RVUs), supply costing and activity-based costing, a more accurate approach versus the past standard of ratio of costs to charges (RCC). Advanced cost accounting is also more timely, providing health systems with information on a more real-time basis rather than the old standard, which was on a semi-annual or annual basis.

When healthcare providers have accurate cost data, they can compare/reduce unnecessary variation in cost per case per physician, identify opportunities to streamline administrative processes and understand labor costs. They can also better analyze the cost to care for patient populations and negotiate more favorable contracts with payers.

However, even with cost data in hand, organizations still struggle to reduce spending unless they take a team approach to cost accounting. Cost reduction efforts take expertise from across the organization, including physicians. One way to engage physicians in the process is simply sharing cost data with them on a comparative basis. If a physician has a high cost per case and sees other physicians performing the same procedures for much lower cost, the high-cost physician can at least begin to start the conversation on what is driving the variance and what it would take to bring costs down.

A poll of the nearly 20 executive roundtable discussion participants revealed the majority of their organizations are sharing information on adverse patient outcomes with physicians. However, the vast majority said cost data is not included in that information.

When physicians are included in the cost conversation, systems can achieve savings. Yale-New Haven (Conn.) Health System has implemented an effective approach to driving out costs. A long-time partner of Strata's, Yale-New Haven Health System implemented Strata's solution at all of its hospitals and hundreds of employed physicians. The system uses quality variation indicators (QVIs) to understand differences in cost based on negative quality outcomes. Through the use of QVIs and other measures, the academic health system has reduced spending by about $150 million, while improving the delivery of care — their number one priority.

The need to bring clinical and financial information together is evident, but roundtable participants indicated that in the past investments in accounting systems were leapfrogged by other purchases. However, with the shift to alternative payment models such as the Comprehensive Care for Joint Replacement model — CMS' first mandatory bundled payment initiative — it is vital hospitals and systems know their costs. Without that information from advanced accounting, providers are indeed "flying blind," said Mr. Michelson, echoing Dr. Porter's 2013 finding.

Republished, with permission, from Becker's Hospital Review, May 9, 2016.

PUT A
DEDICATED
COST LEADER
IN PLACE

3.4

Bending the Cost Curve with the Help of a Dedicated Cost Leader

By Liz Kirk

A recent HIMSS study showed that reducing cost was the top strategic priority for hospitals, academic medical centers, children's hospitals and ambulatory care providers. However, despite this focus, the overwhelming majority of hospitals do not have a senior leader solely dedicated to cost reduction – or even a single person in any department, dedicated to organization-wide cost reduction.

Juxtapose this to the infrastructure of quality improvement. Most hospitals have a vice president of quality and a chief medical officer who dedicate a majority of his or her time to driving quality initiatives. Most providers also have Quality Leaders who collaborate with operational and clinical leaders to drive change, analytics staff that produce quality metrics, and high-functioning quality committees that engage stakeholders and hold initiative owners accountable for achieving goals and for preventing harm events.

But if we look back to the mid-1990s, Quality Improvement looked much like Cost Improvement looks today. There were a few zealots who identified quality issues and tried to drive change. Some hospitals had quality committees too. But without access to data or staff to run the data and lead the projects, these efforts were largely ineffective. Moreover, there were few, if any, widely accepted quality metrics and certainly no goals.

There was little movement in Quality Improvement until 1999 when the Institute of Medicine released their report "To Err is Human." This ground-breaking report exposed the death and harm caused by medical errors and low quality care. From there, the awakening began. The Leapfrog group, The Agency for Healthcare Research and Quality (AHRQ), and others began a national dialogue on quality.

> *Despite being a top strategic priority and despite large investments in EDWs, productivity tools, supply chain and consulting, cost improvement is still in its infancy.*

With this dialogue came a new vocabulary, never before seen transparency, and well-defined metrics that quickly became industry standards. Today, of course, almost every hospital across the country has a robust quality improvement function because that is core to their mission.

Yet, despite being a top strategic priority, despite cost reduction needs that are eight or nine figures, despite large investments in EDWs, productivity tools, supply chain and consulting, cost improvement is still in its infancy. In addition to the lack of staff focused on cost improvement, there is a still a vast gap in knowledge and know-how about strategy and tactics required to drive out cost.

In fact, a recent survey showed that 88 percent of hospitals and health systems had cost reduction goals, but only 17 percent were successfully achieving targets. Over 80 percent were achieving some savings, but were not hitting their targets. Lack of accountability and difficulty in measuring savings were cited as the top drivers of this widespread under-performance.

This is not surprising given the three ways that most hospitals are approaching cost reduction currently:

1. Clinical and operational department leaders leading cost improvements

Projects that significantly reduce cost generally require deep analytics, diligent change management and cross-functional participation. With many other priorities on their plate, department leaders simply cannot dedicate the time or attention to these initiatives and may not have the skill set necessary to do so.

2. Performance improvement leaders leading cost improvements

Some hospitals have staffed cost projects with performance improvement leaders, which typically come from the Quality Improvement department. Two things generally happen which cause savings to fall short. First, the projects chosen will increase efficiency, but not generate measurable cost savings, unless additional actions are taken. One example of this is reducing length of stay. Unless worked hours are reduced or more patients are added, there is no financial impact, other than a reduction in reimbursement from per diem or fee for service payers. Second, projects are often done with a contained scope. While this is good from a project management perspective, critical upstream and downstream processes are often neglected and the impact is limited.

3. Value analysis committees spearheading cost improvements

While the intent is there to drive accountability by engaging a cross functional group with senior leadership sponsorship, results are typically underwhelming because the people tasked with driving the initiatives have too many competing priorities.

I propose that until there are resources dedicated to cost improvement – people who think about driving out cost all day every day – providers will not realize the level of cost savings they need.

Imagine a new role – the Cost Leader

The Cost Leader should align closely with finance, operational and clinical leadership. The Cost Leader should understand what is needed to drive true margin on the income statement, what will and won't work operationally, and how to engage physicians. This role, or department for larger facilities, should have access to financial, clinical and operational data and be able to nimbly pull this data together to identify and quantify cost savings opportunities.

From there, the Cost Leader should work collaboratively with department leaders to validate savings opportunities operationally, and then facilitate implementation of cost improvements. Most importantly, the Cost Leader needs to be an innovator – someone who challenges conventional wisdom, proposes new approaches to old ways of doing things, and can work with operational and clinical leaders to transition these ideas into practice.

Like Quality Improvement, Cost Improvement needs a single senior leader who is responsible for driving cost improvement throughout the organization. His or her role is to garner support from other senior leaders for cost reduction efforts as well as to ensure efforts are coordinated and in sync with other strategic initiatives in the organization.

Also like Quality Improvement, Cost Improvement is highly data intensive, labor intensive and change intensive, yet quite necessary. Unfortunately, the nature of the work and the lack of tools, makes cost reduction costly.

Fortunately, there are applications which are starting to gain traction that will combine large data sets to make complex analyses approachable even to less analytically sophisticated organizations. And other applications on the horizon that run algorithms to find cost savings then continuously measure the savings realized for each initiative and promote accountability by highlighting variance to goals.

These tools will be a game-changer for the cost crisis in healthcare, but they will be most effective in the hands of a dedicated, innovative, collaborative Cost Leader and Cost Improvement Department.

Republished, with permission, from Becker's Hospital Review, November 17, 2014.

3.5

The CIO's Role in

Cost Improvement

By Liz Kirk

INVOLVE CIO AS
A KEY PLAYER

For the last decade, CIOs have been consumed with implementing and gaining adoption for EHRs. Now that they are implemented and widely adopted, we've arrived in the "post-EHR era" — and the CIO's role is shifting.

Now, the CIO's main responsibility is to make all of the data collected day in and day out throughout an organization accessible to decision-makers in an actionable, meaningful and user-friendly format. As the pace of change and degree of risk increases for providers, the need for quick, data-driven decisions grows. Getting data in the hands of operational and clinical leaders will enable improvements in quality, cost and strategy. Whether it's at the bedside or in the executive offices, it is the CIO's duty to get the right information to the right people to provide quality care and make timely, well-informed decisions so the health system runs as effectively and efficiently as possible.

The CIO must be aligned with the strategic priorities of the C-suite. According the annual American College of Healthcare Executives survey, for the 11th year in a row, "financial improvement challenges" topped the list of CEO concerns for 2014, the most recent year available. Not surprisingly, it also tops the list for CFOs, according to several recent surveys.

While CIOs haven't traditionally been financially focused, they are now key players in the cost improvement conversation. The CIO has two vital responsibilities specific to driving out costs: stewardship of the organization-wide IT spend and enabling cost savings initiatives to produce real savings. If a CIO is not viewing his or her role in this way, the organization is undoubtedly not realizing all of the savings available to them.

Stewardship of the IT spend

As healthcare providers become increasingly technology enabled, the opportunities to spend more money on systems, implementation, maintenance fees, networks and consultants are endless. However, the IT stack can quickly become fraught with duplicative systems and functionality — read "excess cost."

After years of cost reduction in front-line operational and clinical areas, it is necessary to look beyond these areas to generate the level of cost savings needed. The CIO should lead the charge to reduce the cost of IT operations.

As shown in Exhibit 1, CIO-related cost savings opportunities run the continuum from straightforward just-do-it actions to the more complex initiatives that require cross-functional collaboration and well defined processes and structures.

The power of the platform in reducing cost

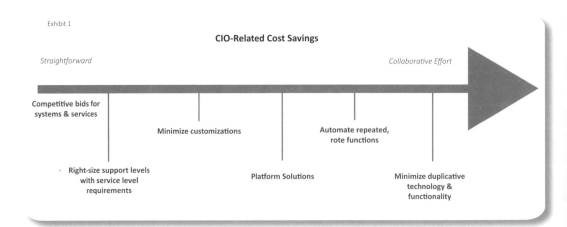

Exhibit 1

CIO-Related Cost Savings

Straightforward — *Collaborative Effort*

Competitive bids for systems & services

Minimize customizations

Automate repeated, rote functions

Right-size support levels with service level requirements

Platform Solutions

Minimize duplicative technology & functionality

One cost savings opportunity that falls directly within the CIO's domain and cannot be overlooked is the power of the platform. Oftentimes, operational, financial or clinical leaders find a system they want that meets their particular needs. But to either feed this system data or use the output of this system, many manual processes are spawned. Smart people become the duct tape that tenuously holds the systems together.

Take the finance operations of a large, academic health system. They have one system for financial decision support, one system for clinical decision support, another system for budgeting, another for long-term financial planning, and yet a fourth system for capital planning and tracking. There are countless manual, offline processes in which a person is critical to moving data from one system to the next. Essential operational reports are routinely run in Excel because no single system supplies the information operational leaders need to manage their department.

Unfortunately, the complexity in this health system is not unique. In fact, it's quite the norm.

It is the CIO's responsibility to provide end users with a better, more efficient, less error-prone process. In the example above, efficiency can be drastically increased by replacing disparate systems with a single platform that provides that functionality all in one.

Reducing customizations

How many times have you heard people in your organization say "we have to customize it to make it work for us" when implementing new systems?

Customizations typically result in higher implementation fees, longer implementation cycles, slower processing times, more support needs, more unplanned downtime and difficulty in upgrading functionality. While it can be difficult to accept off-the-shelf functionality, balancing customizations with standard or supported configurations can result in long-term cost avoidance. It is the CIO's role to help operational and clinical leaders understand this truth and weigh the costs and benefits of requested customizations. Doing so will promote long-term satisfaction with the system.

Simplifying the IT stack to get greater functionality

Having a well-defined methodology for reviewing the existing IT stack and proposals for new systems is an essential CIO duty. The process should include clinical, operational and financial leaders.

Following the DIME method (Exhibit 2) is one example of a rigorous methodology that helps an organization simplify and streamline both existing technologies and evaluate new technologies.

The CIO should require the staff requesting new systems or significant investments in existing systems to provide a business case outlining why the technology is important and the expected ROI on the investment. Clarity and transparency about IT requests,

Exhibit 2

Duplicative Functionality	**I**nnovative Functionality
Does this functionality exist in another system?	Does this system offer new, valuable functionality?
ACTION • Select a single system with the greatest native functionality • May require enhancing features in the selected system	ACTION • Develop a business case • Weigh ROI v. investment v. benefit
System **M**aturity	**E**xisting System or Platform
Where is the system on the maturity scale?	Does the organization already have modules from this vendor?
ACTION • Evaluate if the system is meeting needs and if the vendor is continuing to invest in and enhance the product • Eliminate systems that are not meeting needs	ACTION • Evaluate if there are productivity and functionality benefits to be gained by continuing to invest in the platform rather than going with a best of breed system

including the expected benefits, allows senior leaders to prioritize how scarce dollars are allocated to produce the highest organizational value. Once systems are implemented, the CIO's office should lead a rigorous look-back analysis comparing the forecasted ROI with the realized ROI.

It is equally important for the CIO to partner with operational, clinical and financial leaders as they work to identify and implement cost savings opportunities.

Promoting self-service access to actionable information

Getting useful, drillable, actionable data into the hands of decision-makers is the most impactful endeavor a CIO can take on. When end users have to go through gatekeepers of information to get data, the pace of change slows dramatically and often comes to a complete standstill. Up until recently, these gatekeepers were instrumental because accessing large amounts of data required deep expertise in writing queries and understanding data structures. However, with the introduction of more user-friendly decision support systems and presentation layer software that sits on top of core systems, many end-users can competently access the data they need to make decisions without gatekeeper assistance.

Providing access to self-service data sources and analytical tools will make an organization more action-oriented, data-driven and focused on metrics that matter.

Overcoming 'integration infatuation'

Integration infatuation occurs when recently affiliated organizations make do with sub-standard or inaccurate information and inefficient processes for their combined entities because they are waiting for the same systems to be adopted throughout. This can take years. In the meantime, manual analyses and unwieldy reports are generated by over-taxed teams. Decision-making and progress on important initiatives stall.

The CIO plays a key role in providing a bridge strategy and technologies that enable business leaders to get the information they need — despite the disparate systems — without waiting for years. Technology can pull the same type of data from different systems, normalize it and then make it available for combined reporting and accessible to decision-makers. Major functional areas, such as billing and financial reporting, can be combined easily and the goal of achieving cost savings through affiliating can be realized sooner.

Recognizing the need for niche technology

Despite huge investments in EHRs, new billing systems and enterprise resource planning systems that promise to fulfill virtually all data and process needs, there are niche technologies that go far beyond the off-the-shelf functionality of large, all-purpose vendors. These niche technologies provide sizeable ROIs. For example, there is technology available that sits on top of the core billing system and automates over 50 percent of the tasks that billing staff do on a daily basis — and with greater consistency.

There is also technology available that runs algorithms to find cost savings across an organization and presents these findings in a way clinical and operational people can easily understand and act on, thus minimizing the need for an army of analysts to do math. It is this type of functionality that can truly change the tenor of an organization. Rather than having people grind through data and invest in automating rote work, staff can focus on work that requires their unique expertise and knowledge. In addition to producing savings by requiring fewer FTEs, these niche technologies can also accelerate the pace of change as staff focuses on driving improvements.

Unfortunately, operational leaders often don't get exposure to these new technologies. The CIO should both scan the market for technologies that will streamline and improve major processes, as well as promote thoughtful consideration of proposals that operational leaders bring forward.

Leveraging the right technology for cost improvement

As CIOs look toward the future and how they can make a positive impact, their No. 1 focus should be expediting the flow of meaningful information into the hands of those who need to make decisions — in all areas of the health system. We know for sure that the technology is there to take healthcare to the next level: to make it more efficient, more predictable, more personalized and more automated. It is the responsibility of the CIO to lead the organization forward in this post-EHR era to a brighter future where healthcare is not only more effective, but also more sustainable for many years to come.

Republished, with permission, from Becker's Hospital Review, February 10, 2016.

Name _____

Address _____ Date _____

℞

GAIN
EXECUTIVE
BUY-IN

MD _____

Signature _____

3.6

To Cut Healthcare Costs, Start at the Top

By Rene Letourneau

Financial leaders can identify where and how to trim budgets, but it's up to CEOs to get buy-in from an organization's leadership and staff, and to address the cultural, quality and staffing concerns associated with deep cuts.

As the healthcare industry moves toward value-based reimbursement models, it is becoming increasingly important for hospitals and health systems to find ways to trim as much waste as possible from the cost of doing business.

This reality is reflected in a recent survey from Strata Decision Technology in which 88 percent of respondents said their organizations have established cost-reduction targets.

But, while the overwhelming majority of provider organizations are trying to cut cost, according to the survey, not many are achieving their objectives: Only 17 percent of respondents rated their organization as successful, and 69 percent said they are just somewhat successful in reaching their goals.

Among the key reasons cited for this shortfall are difficulty tracking results (55%); lack of accountability (44%); inconsistent focus from senior leaders (30%), and lack of clinician engagement (29%).

Finding new efficiencies

One of the organizations that participated in the survey is Mission Health System, a six-hospital system based in Asheville, NC.

"We started our budget process several weeks ago and determined we have a $52 million need for improvement for the system, and I would say the majority of that is to come through cost reduction rather than enhanced revenue," says Larry Hill, Mission's vice president of finance. "This is the target we need to get to over the next three years to keep our margin at what I would call a healthy system margin."

To reach this goal, Hill expects Mission will reduce its supply chain spending by $5.3 million this fiscal year and will look at making cuts to its workforce.

"We did not go into the process predisposed as to where the cost would need to come from, but we know that some of it will be labor-driven," he says. "There will be people in positions that will be restructured out of the workforce, and then there will be some taken out through attrition and currently vacant positions."

Mission is also centralizing many of its administrative and support services in areas such as IT and revenue cycle operations in order to "remove all the duplication," Hill says.

"These services are being collapsed and streamlined to a corporate model. We've been consolidating our financial systems and EMRs. What has been more difficult has been on the outpatient side with registration and billing because there are so many billing practices attached to legacy systems. From an IT perspective, we are nowhere near best practices on the number of systems we are supporting, and we know there is quite a bit of waste and redundancy that we can eliminate there."

When I asked Hill about the survey and why he thinks it appears to be so difficult for healthcare organizations to achieve their cost-reduction goals, he said it comes back to communication from the CEO to staff around the reasons for the cuts and what they mean for the long-term health of the organization.

Mission set out to put the patient first and to focus on quality and safety, and that will not be compromised by trying to achieve cost reduction targets.

"We started the budget process with a series of mandatory town hall meetings that were conducted by our CEO, and he explained the current state of affairs, how we are going to approach the process, and at the same time, he made a promise that the short-term, one-time measure we took last year of not giving pay increases would not be deployed again. He asked for partnership from the leadership and staff, and we are definitely getting buy-in."

Cost reductions shouldn't threaten quality

Hill says it is also important to make sure employees understand that cost-containment efforts are not being made at the expense of quality.

"We have invested so much in quality and outcomes, and we cannot regress on that," he says. "Mission set out to put the patient first and to focus on quality and safety, and that will not be compromised by trying to achieve cost-reduction targets."

Michael Sitowitz, controller at Parrish Medical Center, a 210-bed acute care hospital in Titusville, FL, agrees that it's important to be sure that any efforts to reduce spending do not have a negative impact on quality. PMC also participated in the survey.

"You can't just look at cost and say you are going to cut cost out because you have to have a value equation that also looks at quality, safety and outcomes. It's real easy to say you are going to cut cost, but you have to look at what is potentially going to suffer," Sitowitz says, noting that PMC uses Lean Six Sigma to find process improvements and pull waste out of the system.

PMC has operated for nearly twelve years under what it calls its "strategic game plan" – the guiding principles it uses to ensure it is providing high-quality, low-cost care, Sitowitz says.

"Although it is a small group of people who created this plan, we spoke to a lot of our clinicians and physicians about how making changes in processes would impact care. We asked if these were processes they could adopt. We really took the time to make sure we were not just implementing a strategy the hospital thought was right but that all of our stakeholders could support," he says of how PMC achieved organization-wide buy-in for its game plan from the start.

Providing clinicians with data to help them realize that using a lot of expensive resources does not always equate to better care also goes a long way toward achieving cost-reduction goals, Sitowitz says.

"The best way to talk to them is with evidenced-based information that shows that outcomes are similar or better [with the use of fewer resources], and that is how you can move the conversation along."

Succeeding in a value-based world

When I asked Sitowitz about the survey results, like Hill at Mission Health, he said he believes successfully rolling out new strategies to cut costs and improve quality begins at the top. He credits PMC's CEO and senior administrators for creating a culture that is able to adapt as needed in the new value-driven healthcare environment and where everyone understands they have a part to play in keeping costs down.

"Our CEO looked at the new building that we built in 2002, and he realized that just because you move into a new building, it doesn't change your culture. So when the new facility opened, he began a two- to three-year journey to really get people to understand what our culture needs to be for us to be successful in the future," he says.

"Now, our leadership group meets every month to go over how people are doing, where people are doing well, and where they are struggling. We talk about strategies to resolve any issues, and we all talk about all areas of the organization, not just our own, because we are all responsible for our overall success."

By Rene Letourneau, originally published September 8, 2014.
Reprinted with permission from HealthLeaders Media.

3.7

Making Cost of Care Less Expensive for Hospitals

By Liz Kirk

UTILIZE ACTIONABLE DATA TO DRIVE ACCOUNTABILITY

As hospitals and ACOs try to reduce the cost of care as they take on more risk, conversations about utilization are front and center. However, as we are working tirelessly to make the cost of care lower by right-sizing utilization, are we actually making care more expensive?

The answer is "yes" – unless your organization is a lean, mean flexing machine that can define lower-cost ways of providing high-quality care.

As hospitals see declines in overall admissions, their focus should shift to reducing their expense base to accommodate lower volumes.

Reducing utilization will reduce the total charges on a patient's bill. Depending on the reimbursement methodology used, it reduces the amount the insurer pays the provider. But it does not necessarily reduce the cost of care. It actually may increase the cost of care for patients who are seen at the hospital in the future.

Let's look at a common example. A mid-sized hospital focuses on reducing readmissions for the Centers for Medicare & Medicaid Services-designated conditions for reimbursement penalties. Their readmission rate for these cases is 20 percent – not out of line with most other facilities, but still needing some work.

They pull together teams of physicians, nurses, administrators and case managers and reduce readmissions in those DRGs by 30 percent. They have reduced more than 1,600 patient days. Patients and payers are now receiving at least $4 million less in charges.

However, with 1,600 fewer patient days (approximately 4.3 fewer patients per day), has the hospital taken out a commensurate level of cost? Now compound this with the reduction in utilization from other initiatives that are under way to reduce utilization, such as reducing ICU days and hospital admissions for patients at the end of life, assigning medical homes to prevent admissions for chronic conditions and reducing length of stay for ACO enrollees.

The bottom line is that revenue will decline along with patient admissions and inpatient days.

The clear call to action is that expense reductions need to keep pace. Unless the largest cost driver, which is staffing, is going down in lock step with the reduction in volume, your organization's cost of care is not going down. Rather, the same cost is being spread over fewer patient days, fewer lab tests, fewer drugs administered and therefore the cost of each individual service for each patient seen in the future increases.

And here's where the problem really begins. The unfortunate truth is that most hospitals are not highly effective in flexing staff down when volume declines. Nor are they particularly adept at implementing lower-cost models of care.

It's hard to adjust staff schedules, to cut hours, to ask staff not to come to work, to ask staff to leave early, to take PTO when they don't want to, and of course, to lay people off. It is even harder for department leaders who know that if volume spikes and staffing is low, patients' lives could be jeopardized.

Moreover, department administrators don't typically have the detailed information needed to provide them insight into their actual staffing needs based on volume trends and service mix, not to mention the data needed, and time to analyze the data, to identify opportunities to reduce labor costs beyond simply flexing down. Without data to project the likely impact of reducing staffing, department leaders often don't have the confidence to move forward with lower-cost staffing models.

The path forward is to leverage analytics to combine large data sets, pull out meaningful trends, and produce highly visual charts that point department leaders to specific opportunities to reduce cost. Sustainable cost reduction involves more than staffing to volume, but more importantly, re-thinking how care is delivered.

Once improvements are defined, having readily accessible and actionable data to drive accountability for achieving results is absolutely critical. Only then will healthcare providers be able to build a culture of continuous cost improvement and truly be able to reduce the cost of care, not just amount paid for care.

Republished, with permission, from Healthcare Finance News, March 26, 2014.

ENGAGE
PHYSICIANS

3.8

Why Hospital Cost Containment Efforts Depend on Physicians

By Ayla Ellison

With risk-based models like bundled payments gaining speed, hospitals and health systems need to reexamine their cost cutting strategies and include physicians in cost containment conversations.

"The business model of healthcare is changing," said Strata Decision Technology CEO Dan Michelson during a recent webinar hosted by *Becker's Hospital Review*. He illustrated the pace of change by zeroing in on the Medicare Hospital Value-Based Purchasing Program and mandatory bundled payment programs to highlight how the healthcare landscape is shifting.

The Hospital Value-Based Purchasing Program, established under the Affordable Care Act, is intended to encourage hospitals to provide high-quality care more efficiently by adjusting payments to hospitals based on the quality of care they provide. In fiscal year 2016, more than 1,800 hospitals will receive a positive payment adjustment under the program.

CMS also implemented its first mandatory bundled payment initiative, the Comprehensive Care for Joint Replacement model, in April. This is an attempt by CMS to reduce variation in costs for hip and knee replacements, since the average Medicare expenditure for surgery, hospitalization and recovery ranges from $16,500 to $33,000 across geographic areas.

Under the payment model, acute care hospitals are held accountable for the quality of care they deliver to Medicare beneficiaries for hip and knee replacement from surgery through recovery. Depending on the hospital's quality and spending performance, the hospital may receive an additional payment from Medicare or be required to repay Medicare for a portion of the spending. In late July 2016, CMS proposed a new mandatory bundled payment program for heart attacks and bypass surgeries that includes changes to the existing CJR model.

The confusion around "cost" begins with its definition. When hospital leaders discuss costs, some refer to price, while others refer to charges or reimbursement.

Under these new payment models, reimbursement is linked to health outcomes, requiring hospitals and health systems to take a much closer look at quality and cost data to deliver more efficient care.

Confusion around cost

The conversation around cost is confusing, and it is hard to know what "value" actually means until that conversation is normalized, according to Mr. Michelson.

The confusion around "cost" begins with its definition. When hospital leaders discuss costs, some refer to price, while others refer to charges or reimbursement.

The first step to designing an effective cost containment strategy is arriving at a common definition of the term. Next, organizations need to ensure the cost information they're relying on is accurate. Mr. Michelson expanded on this point by sharing a cartoon of SpongeBob he saw on his daughter's Instagram account.

SpongeBob and his friend Patrick, a starfish, stare at what appears to be thousands of mattresses. In the cartoon, SpongeBob says to Patrick, "Wow Patrick look at all of these mattresses! How many do you think there are?" Patrick replies, "Ten." SpongeBob responds, "Cool."

The cartoon reminded Mr. Michelson of healthcare, because in the absence of accurate cost information, any number will do. However, without accurate information, systems will see their cost saving efforts fail.

Including physicians in the cost conversation

Although cost reduction has moved to the top of many organizations' priorities, a number of missteps can cause cost containment efforts to flounder. Advanced cost accounting software can help hospitals and health systems reach their cost reduction goals, but technology alone cannot render effective change without new ways of thinking.

Hospital leaders who have been given the seemingly impossible task of improving quality with fewer resources must bring physicians into the loop, said Neel Shah, MD, an OB/GYN and founder and executive director of CostsOfCare.org, which curates and disseminates knowledge from patients and frontline clinicians to help health systems deliver better care at lower cost.

"The way physicians are taught teaches us to be terrible stewards of resources," said Dr. Shah. However, he said people on the frontline, including physicians, have ideas for how to provide more affordable care.

To highlight Dr. Shah's point, Mr. Michelson referenced a *Health Affairs* report, which revealed physicians control 80 percent of the spend in U.S. healthcare, but only one in five can correctly estimate the cost of common orthopedic devices. The study shows that systems can achieve savings when physicians are included in the cost conversation, as 80 percent of physicians said cost was a key criterion in the selection of a medical device.

Yale-New Haven (Conn.) Health System, a long-time partner of Strata's, has seen its cost containment efforts succeed by including physicians in the conversation. "Our organization knew back in 2008 that we were going to have pressure on our revenue," said Stephen Allegretto, vice president of strategic analytics and financial planning at Yale-New Haven Health System. The system addressed the issue head on.

After implementing an EMR and establishing a common definition of quality, Yale-New Haven implemented Strata's solution systemwide. The academic health system now uses quality value indicators (QVIs™) to understand differences in cost based on negative quality outcomes. Through the use of QVIs and by including physicians in the cost conversation, Yale-New Haven has reduced spending by about $150 million, while improving the delivery of care — its No. 1 priority.

Republished, with permission, from Becker's Hospital Review, August 3, 2016.

3.9

Improving Clinicians' Access to Cost Data

By John Kenagy, Ben Shah and Dan Michelson

It is important to focus on easy wins at the beginning of the project.

In the past, the director of the orthopedics service line at Legacy Health in Portland, OR, had to rely on a reporting analyst – and often had to wait in line – if she wanted to know how standardizing a hip implant might affect her service line's financial and clinical outcomes. But now, she can run her own reports instantly and take greater ownership of her department's performance using business intelligence (BI) tools that draw cost and quality data from the system's enterprise data warehouse (EDW).

Although all health systems want to place actionable data directly in the hands of service line leaders, doing so requires thorough planning and forward-thinking leadership. Here are some strategies that organizations can use to empower clinicians and service line leaders with integrated cost and clinical data, based on lessons learned from Legacy's ongoing BI strategy.

Create a vision

Giving clinicians access to cost and quality data as part of a broader BI strategy requires a clear vision and leaders who are willing to commit the time and resources. The vision should center on finding effective ways to marry clinical and financial data into usable information that clinicians and service line leaders can use to improve their performance and make healthcare delivery more consistent – and less costly.

Legacy's BI strategy was guided by such a vision: System leaders wanted to provide their clinical teams with access to cost data and tools that would help them make good decisions in an environment increasingly focused on value. The philosophy was not entirely new. Legacy's leaders have long viewed the organization's electronic health record (EHR) as a value strategy, not an IT strategy, and this mindset helped drive EHR adoption across Legacy's six hospitals and more than 50 ambulatory clinics, laboratories and hospice facilities.

Although Legacy had access to clinical data due to the success of its EHR rollout, the health system still struggled to put practical, actionable cost data in the hands of clinical leaders. Legacy's vision was to integrate the financial data from its costing system with clinical data from its EHR in a single EDW and then to provide physicians with "self-service" BI tools that would enable them to access cost data in the EDW and model the financial impact of their decisions. It was an ambitious goal that required collaboration with leaders from multiple disciplines as well as with two separate vendors for the EHR and the costing system.

Create a workgroup and host a "jam session"

Getting costing and clinical systems to "talk" to each other requires the combined efforts of technical, financial and clinical experts, ideally assembled into a workgroup focused on the larger BI strategy. Members of the BI workgroup should be highly engaged so they can help define what can be an ambiguous project. BI means different things to different people, and members tend to be focused on their own needs. Together, the workgroup can get to the core of what matters to the organization and determine which cost information to share with clinicians and how to do it.

Legacy's workgroup meets monthly and includes leaders from finance, quality, IT, operations and the medical group. Earlier this year, the workgroup convened what it called a two-day "jam session" at Legacy with the health system's EHR and decision support vendors, as well as with clinicians from Legacy's care transformation group, which leads the system's population health strategy.

Without using specific terminology, the clinicians told the workgroup and vendors that they wanted predictive analytics tools that would help them weigh the financial impact of their decisions. Specifically, they wanted access to cost data at the disease, diagnosis and patient levels so they could understand the ROI of their initiatives. For example, they wanted to know:

- How reducing admissions of diabetes patients by 10 percent through better outpatient management might affect cost

- What efficiencies might be gained if knee implants were standardized

- Whether adding case managers to coordinate care might reduce readmissions and negatively affect the organization's bottom line

To gain such insights, they decided to model various scenarios using historical data and trends as a guide. During the jam session, the workgroup conducted several test runs of the cost data and was able to quantify value in several service areas by using quality as the numerator and cost as the denominator. Specifically, the workgroup used length of stay (LOS) as the quality indicator and measured cost relative to LOS.

Share the most actionable data

Robust financial platforms can collect many different "buckets" of finance data. Although highly useful to financial managers, these cost components can overwhelm clinicians, who can have the most impact in two areas: labor and supply costs. Thus, it is critical to limit which financial information is pulled from the costing system into the EDW for clinicians to access and assess.

Before integrating data from different sources, the BI workgroup and finance team need to determine how they will define certain data points. Strong data governance ensures that everyone is using the same cost data definitions before the technical experts and vendors begin building models and tools. Take the cost of a prescription drug, for example. Clinical, financial and IT leaders need to agree on what exactly that cost is: Is it the unit cost of the medication, the cost of the medication plus labor, the out-of-pocket cost to the patient, or the charge to the patient? Such discussions are essential to ensuring the validity of the cost data.

> *Strong data governance ensures that everyone is using the same cost data definitions before the technical experts and vendors begin building models and tools.*

When determining which cost data to share with clinicians, it is important to ask three questions:

1. Do clinicians have an impact on the cost?

2. How were the cost data determined? (For example, was the supply cost pulled directly from the supply chain, or was it allocated from the general ledger using statistics?)

3. How granular should the cost data be for clinicians? (For example, is total labor cost enough, or will clinicians need breakdowns of nursing, administrative and physician labor costs?)

The BI workgroup and finance team at Legacy narrowed the list of cost data available to clinicians. The final list included:

- Direct labor costs (cost of physicians, nurses, pharmacists and other caregivers)

- Direct supply costs (cost of medications, implants, needles and other supplies)

- Other direct costs (IT, utilities and purchased services such as contract janitorial labor)

- Total direct costs (sum of direct labor costs, direct supply costs and other direct costs)

- Total indirect costs (overhead, including administrative, housekeeping and finance)

They chose to omit more financially-oriented cost components, such as bad debt, depreciation and indirect overhead expenses, which clinicians cannot control.

Hire and reorganize BI staff

Integrating cost and clinical data from various systems requires the skills of a BI architect, who can design the framework of a BI platform. Ideally, a BI architect should demonstrate:

- Strong visualization and organizational skills

- Excellent listening skills and a consultative mindset that can help unravel needs that are not always well-stated by clinical leaders

- Experience with healthcare cost and quality data

Finding a BI architect who possesses these qualities can be challenging in a competitive market. For this reason, organizations may need to groom an individual from within the ranks of IT to take on this key role.

Legacy hired a BI architect from the technology industry, which has been using BI effectively for many years. The BI architect was highly effective at working with vendors to build the infrastructure for clinicians to access the data. For the health system's cost data, for example, the architect wrote an integration process that transferred information from the financial platform to the data warehouse via a secure file transfer protocol (FTP).

Other members of Legacy's technical team who have worked on the project include a BI manager, several programmers and senior business analysts, and 10 reporting analysts. Until recently, the reporting analysts focused primarily on developing custom reports for the service lines. But Legacy redeployed several reporting analysts to help develop the self-service model for clinical leaders to access their cost data. These reporting analysts also are training clinicians on how to build their reports. In essence, they have become the heart of a virtual BI "think tank" at Legacy.

Having an individual who can bridge the finance and IT teams also is highly valuable. At Legacy, the finance director who had led the implementation of the costing system was transferred to the organization's IT department to help guide the development of the BI platform.

Educate clinicians on costs and BI

Getting clinicians to make the most of the cost data requires education and support regarding costing methodologies and an understanding of what "cost" means. Business intelligence is a new concept for some clinicians, particularly those in not-for-profit health systems, who may get turned off by the "corporate" feel of the term. For this reason, education is vitally important to the success of a BI strategy that places integrated cost and clinical data directly in the hands of physicians.

The finance team at Legacy has been working with the senior director of the medical group to develop a "Cost Accounting 101" course for its hospitalists. The class is designed to promote greater accountability by showing hospitalists how their decisions affect cost and quality outcomes. The class also provides a forum for clinicians to offer suggestions back to the IT team. For instance, some hospitalists have suggested that the health system populate the EHR with the costs of lab tests and pharmaceuticals, along with outcomes information, to help hospitalists make more informed decisions at the bedside.

Legacy developed a "Cost Accounting 101" course for their hospitalists to promote greater accountability by showing hospitalists how their decisions affect cost and quality outcomes.

After a six-month implementation, Legacy's EDW has become home to the system's cost and clinical data. However, the BI team is still rolling out decision support tools to clinicians, starting with "super users" in the medical group, quality team, and other areas. This gradual approach allows leaders at Legacy to ensure that clinicians genuinely understand the cost data and how to use it.

Focus on an easy win at the start

To gain system-wide adoption of BI tools that use cost data, it is best to select a discrete pilot project that can become an "easy win." Orthopedics often is a good place to start because of its high costs, range of supplies, and wide variation in clinical practices and cost among clinicians.

To test the capabilities of the new BI platform at Legacy, an administrative fellow and a supply chain leader are working with the orthopedics service line administrator to review surgical costs and variations in clinical pathways that may present opportunities to contain supply costs.

Legacy also is piloting a tool in orthopedics that allows clinicians to query their cost and quality data via a self-service "universe." Users enrolled in the pilot can access this universe via a secure web link and create custom reports using an intuitive interface. Specifically, they can build reports using "drag and drop" data fields that represent patient demographics, costs, and other metrics. Clinicians can click on each data field to get the definition of that element, which helps reduce ambiguity.

Grow BI to meet your needs

Over time, a BI platform that makes cost and quality data available to clinicians should be scalable and adaptable as data, technology and users become more sophisticated.

This year, leaders at Legacy hope to add patient satisfaction data to the EDW so clinicians can use satisfaction, quality and cost data to inform their strategic decisions. The BI team also expects to make enhancements to the BI platform when the system fills key positions for a vice president of quality and a population health analyst.

Ultimately, the BI team at Legacy wants clinicians to see value in having integrated cost and clinical data at their disposal. One measure of success will be whether clinical leaders use the BI tools to access cost data during the budgeting process early next year. The tools may help them make decisions such as whether to hire a new clinician, whether to close a program, and whether to limit services to just a few hospitals in the system or partner with another organization that is stronger in that service area.

The end goal is to have clinical leaders access the cost data on their own and make decisions based on information they trust rather than consensus or gut instincts.

Developing a BI platform that empowers clinicians with cost and quality data requires an up-front investment, but leaders at Legacy believe a self-service approach is more efficient and effective than having reporting analysts run reports and "own" the data.

Ultimately, organizations that are able to marry their cost and quality data will have a strategic advantage as the pressure on margins increases, even if they choose not to implement a self-service BI solution like Legacy's solution. With a clearer picture of their financial and clinical performance, these organizations will be better prepared to develop realistic strategies to meet their goals and demonstrate value to their customers.

Why Physicians and Finance Executives Need to Work Together

By Bob Herman

BRING
PHYSICIANS
AND FINANCE
TOGETHER

When Neel Shah, MD, an OB/GYN, was a resident at Brigham and Women's Hospital in Boston, he encountered a patient who had an ectopic pregnancy – a potential medical emergency for the mother in which the embryo is not in the uterus.

The patient asked Dr. Shah how much treatment was going to cost, and he hit a wall. He had no idea what the cost of care was. As a resident, he and many others abide by the Hippocratic Oath to first, do no harm, and always keep the patient's health and safety at the forefront. In training, he says physicians simply are not trained to think about the cost, or financial well-being, of their patients. This lack of knowledge "eroded [the patient's] trust in me," Dr. Shah said.

"You spend a quarter century in the classroom, and you have an idea of what being a doctor was going to be like," said Dr. Shah, 31. "But there's this huge disconnect."

Dr. Shah, and many other physicians-in-training, have been frustrated with this side of medicine. Roughly one-third of all healthcare spending, or approximately $800 billion every year, is spent on tests and treatments that do nothing to help patient care, yet the medical culture encourages this type of waste. In the process, medical bills continue to be the leading cause of personal bankruptcies in the United States. It translates into a loss for patients, healthcare organizations and society at large.

A few years ago, Dr. Shah founded Costs of Care, a non-profit organization that aims to help clinicians and patients "deflate medical bills."

Roughly 1/3 of all healthcare spending, or approximately $800 billion every year, is spent on tests and treatments that do nothing to help patient care, yet the medical culture encourages this type of waste.

"Physicians are increasingly willing to partner with financial managers, and for the sake of all of us – patients, institutions – we need to find new ways to merge our knowledge," said Dr. Shah, who is now a practicing OB/GYN at Beth Israel Deaconess Medical Center in Boston.

Physicians haven't traditionally shared a lunch table with hospital CFOs and their finance teams. The shift to value-based healthcare means the two sides will have to be on the same team, he said, and there are several ways to collaborate. For instance, hospitals must tell physicians what different procedures and treatments cost. As Dr. Shah mentioned, physicians are not trained to think of cost when diagnosing a patient – in fact, it's considered "taboo." Although prices and evidence of value-based care may not be enough to change a physician's habits, it's a good starting point, Dr. Shah said.

Finance executives and physicians can also look at evidence-based studies and administrative data to validate new behaviors. Dr. Shah used the example of Caesarean sections. C-sections, which are predominantly ordered by physicians, are the most common major surgery in healthcare – but a majority of them are not necessary. In fact, several healthcare organizations have said the United States could save $5 billion in maternity costs if C-section rates were more in line with global recommendations.

In the end, providers need to bring an "environmentalism" aspect to healthcare, Dr. Shah said. He compared today's medical residents to environmentalists of the 1960s, who drastically helped change public policy and perception toward conservation. People who litter on the street are bound to get nasty looks from bystanders, and similarly, healthcare professionals need the same kind of pressure to reign in the bloating costs of wasteful practices.

"Medical residents are climbing a learning curve, and like me, they are questioning everything," Dr. Shah said. "There's a social responsibility to wrap our heads around it."

Republished, with permission, from Becker's Hospital Review, October 23, 2013.

PART FOUR
Driving To and Delivering Value

4.0 Overview

By Liz Kirk

A quote from the futurist William Ford Gibson perfectly captures the state of healthcare: "The future is here, it's just not evenly distributed." In many ways and in many places, the value-based model of care we seek in the future is here right now. The question is how to find that roadmap to get there.

The good news is that there are examples everywhere of how leading health systems have stepped into the future, providing a path for others to follow. These trailblazers are showing how understanding true costs can help illustrate how spending more does not equate to better quality and how organizations can identify opportunities to reduce costs without negatively impacting clinical outcomes. Said differently, they are showing the path to value.

These organizations are showing how to bring clinical and financial data together in a meaningful way. They are taking steps to ensure their clinical, financial and operational leaders all have access to data so they can work in collaboration versus live in conflict. They are showing how to use this data in the community to improve the health of the population over time vs. the care for a single patient on a single visit.

Driving margin and mission requires not just ideas, but action. While the journey to the most effective use of the limited resources we have is often laden with twists, turns, blind alleys, and no clear map, the stories highlighted in this section provide best practices in ensuring financial resources line up to drive margin to fuel mission:

- Reduce cost by improving quality – p. 153

- Understand the total cost of care to deliver value – p. 165

- Employ a service line managment structure – p. 170

- Sustain operating margin – p. 182

- Improve across the continuum – p. 189

- Use protocols – p. 193

4.1

Looking at Variation Through a Quality Lens

By Dan Michelson and Steve Allegretto

Learning to speak the same language on cost and quality metrics has helped clinical and finance leaders at Yale-New Haven Health System reduce variation, improve patient outcomes and decrease overall costs.

Over the past two years, leaders at Yale-New Haven Health System, New Haven, CT, have turned a corner in their efforts to engage physicians and nurses in reducing unnecessary clinical practice variation. Leaders were able to initiate meaningful and productive conversations with clinicians through a simple shift in focus – specifically, looking at clinical and cost variation through a quality lens first.

This focus on quality is at the center of Yale-New Haven's multi-year, $125 million cost-savings plan, designed to reduce the health system's cost per case by about 20 percent. To get there, leaders at the three-hospital system are relying on a customized set of quality metrics, coupled with a sophisticated cost accounting system and other tools, to partner with clinical leaders in reducing variation, improving outcomes and decreasing costs.

Like Yale-New Haven, other health systems around the country serving large Medicare and Medicaid populations are looking for better ways to collaborate with clinicians on quality improvement and cost reduction. Finance leaders in particular recognize the critical importance of fully engaging clinical leaders to help their organizations prepare for changes resulting from healthcare reform and the move toward value-based payment models. Yale-New Haven's experience points to strategies finance leaders can use to successfully partner with clinical leaders around cost and quality.

Using metrics called quality variation indicators to translate negative quality outcomes into measurable costs, organizations can create a basis for communication on improving quality and reducing costs.

Identify key quality targets

When hospital finance leaders share data on clinical variation, they often face significant skepticism from physicians about whether the data truly reflect their experiences with their patients. Physicians also tend to become impatient when finance leaders talk about cost per case instead of topics that reflect quality concerns, such as waste and the need to reduce clinical complications. Finance leaders are prone to be skeptical as well, often questioning whether quality improvements can lead to improved margins through reductions in labor and non-labor costs. This skepticism on both sides can obstruct effective communication.

At Yale-New Haven, finance leaders have met this challenge by developing a common language around clinical quality and variation that makes it easier for finance and clinical leaders to understand each other. The language is based on metrics they developed called quality variation indicators (QVIs).

Simply defined, QVIs are potentially preventable complications and adverse events that occur in patients. To identify the QVIs, a team of physicians and decision support nurses spent three months reviewing a comprehensive list of hospital-acquired conditions, patient safety indicators, and other negative outcomes that were associated with significant variation in quality across the organization. Today, the system tracks nearly 30 QVI categories – such as central line-associated blood stream infections, deep vein thrombosis, and iatrogenic pneumothorax (a punctured lung) – for all payers. This approach gives finance and clinical leaders a shared basis for discussing how quality and waste affect both utilization of services and overall cost per case.

The QVIs help clinical and operations leaders of each cost center understand the indicators' influence on various quality metrics. Each month, cost center and service line leaders receive reports in their monthly financial statements that detail the costs of cases that have a QVI and those that do not. On average, a case with a QVI will cost three to four times as much as a case without a QVI.

Before having the QVIs in place, leaders knew that cost varied within patient populations, but they could not attribute the variation to a particular quality issue. The QVIs allow finance leaders to have meaningful conversations with physicians and other clinical leaders about quality and its impact on cost. They also enable the finance team to measure how quality improvements affect financial outcomes, such as cost per case.

By sharing this information with clinicians, health system leaders hope to drive change that promotes improved quality while reducing costly clinical complications and waste. The leaders are careful not to assign responsibility for a QVI to a particular physician or provider, because a QVI may have occurred at any point during the process of caring for a patient.

The integrated QVI data allow the organization to translate how specific quality improvement and waste reduction efforts affect patient specific costs. In the past, physicians and clinical leaders would spend much time arguing with the finance team about the validity of the data. Now, physicians and clinicians recognize that the data offer an accurate picture of the types of patients they see daily, making them much more receptive to viewing finance as a partner in their efforts to improve patient care.

Find enthusiastic clinical redesign champions

Reducing variation to improve quality and reduce costs often requires the redesign and standardization of clinical processes. For this reason, hospitals should appoint clinical leaders and teams who can review clinical outcomes and cost data and propose appropriate practice changes.

Leading the clinical redesign efforts at Yale-New Haven is Thomas Balcezak, MD, senior vice president and chief quality officer. A physician with a deep interest in healthcare delivery and finance, Balcezak helps guide physician-led clinical redesign teams. These teams, which focus on specific areas such as major joint surgery and sickle cell anemia care, are charged with examining clinical practice, reviewing integrated data, and recommending strategies to reduce inappropriate variation.

A robust cost accounting system facilitates improved communication between clinical and finance leaders by enabling them to see variation related to clinical processes, outcomes and cost of care. "We were surprised by how often we saw those three areas overlap – areas where we knew we needed to improve processes of care, as well as clinical and financial outcomes," Balcezak says. "We decided to target those areas of overlap first so we could demonstrate to the institution that targeting costs did not mean there would be any degradation of quality of care. By focusing on those areas, we have been able to convince clinicians to continue to partner with us on our clinical redesign projects."

When developing a clinical redesign project, leaders at Yale-New Haven seek out an engaged clinician to lead the initiative.

Determining the ROI of a Clinical Redesign Project

Improvements/Reductions

| Quality Variation | Process Variation | Revenue Impact | Backfill Opportunity |

ROI =

Operating | Investments | Capital

Analytics

External   Internal

Costs

"When we find the right leader, we show that individual the QVIs and the detailed cost accounting that we have done, as well as the payment arrangements or the quality program that influences how the revenue flows for this patient population, Balcezak says. "Then we search for opportunities where we can simultaneously improve the experience, outcomes and finances for that group of patients."

System-wide, leaders at Yale-New Haven are focusing their early efforts to reduce clinical variation on three main areas: blood utilization management, palliative care and care in and outside of the intensive care unit (ICU). More than 30 physician- and nursing-led clinical redesign projects at the three hospitals are centered on improving care related to abdominal surgery, hip fractures, emergency department (ED) admissions and more.

For example, one physician led the cardiac clinical redesign team's efforts to improve the appropriate use of bivalirudin, an agent that can reduce the risks of bleeding after surgery in at-risk patients, according to published clinical trials, but that is often used in patients with a low risk of bleeding. At Yale-New Haven, an analysis revealed that physicians who prescribed bivalirudin about 90 percent of the time or more for patients with a high risk of bleeding also ordered it 90 percent of the time or more for patients at a low risk of bleeding. Meanwhile, there were instances where physicians actually were prescribing bivalirudin to a greater percentage of patients at low risk of bleeding than to patients at high risk.

> *Yale-New Haven increased overall appropriate use of bivalirudin by nearly 30 percent, contributing to a reduction in direct cost per case for these patients.*

The physician leader partnered with the finance team to create monthly reports showing the variation, which has helped to encourage more appropriate prescribing of the drug. In addition, a portion of the clinical department's performance arrangement is tied to appropriate bivalirudin use. As a result of these efforts, Yale-New Haven increased overall appropriate use of bivalirudin by nearly 30 percent, contributing to a reduction in direct cost per case for these patients.

Look for early wins and capitalize on success

Deciding which areas of variation to focus on can be a challenge for many organizations. Ideally, hospitals should look for projects that can generate results early to help build momentum and clinician buy-in.

One example of an "early win" at Yale-New Haven was an initiative for patients with sickle cell disease that improved patient outcomes and achieved a $1.9 million cost improvement during a two-year period. The sickle cell clinical redesign team standardized hydration and infection-control protocols in a dedicated, 20-bed unit for these patients. The team also improved care coordination by giving recently discharged patients around-the-clock phone access to a physician and two mid-level providers with specialized expertise in sickle cell conditions. As a result, the clinical redesign team was able to cut length of stay (LOS) for patients with sickle cell disease by 25 percent in the unit and backfill beds with patients with other conditions. The team also reduced ED utilization by 20 percent and increased primary care visits among patients with sickle cells by 20 percent.

As another example, one of the health system's hospitals has had significant success in reducing ventilator-associated pneumonia (VAP) through a new protocol implemented in 2013. Specifically, clinical leaders changed the order set in the electronic health record (EHR) to include different sedative medications and early mobilization to get patients moving more quickly. As a result of these efforts, the number of VAP cases in the surgical ICU (SICU) dropped from 11 to four over the period of 2012 to 2013, saving approximately $200,000 in labor and $500,000 in non-labor costs, including respiratory therapy costs. As VAP cases decreased, the SICU nurse manager appropriately managed staffing ratios to match patient demand, demonstrating that better quality can lead to lower costs.

Having "poster projects" like these has helped leaders at Yale-New Haven build momentum for current projects, including an initiative focused on managing outcomes and costs among joint replacement patients. The health system has built a registry to track the functional status of joint replacement patients before and after surgery. By measuring these data and adding other patient outcome measures in the future, the system hopes to demonstrate to payers that it can improve quality and reduce costs in this high-profile population.

With respect to ROI, Yale-New Haven's leaders initially set a goal to achieve an 8-to-1 return on each clinical redesign project. For example, initiatives that require a $100,000 investment (in staff, technology and the like) need to generate $800,000 in savings that can be attributed to improved performance in at least one of four areas: quality variation, process, revenue and backfill. Of course, not every clinical project will meet its targeted ROI. But clinical and finance leaders can still learn from these initiatives and keep moving forward.

Help leaders become CEOs of their units

To drive cost savings at the cost center level, nursing leaders need to be part of the discussions on variation. The reason is simple: Although organizations need physician partnerships to make clinical process changes, nursing and other clinical leaders have the organizational responsibility to translate those utilization and practice changes into real cost improvements. For example, if LOS decreases due to a clinical redesign process, the only way for this change to translate into meaningfully reduced cost is if nurse managers realign labor and non-labor resources on their unit.

Yale-New Haven's leaders learned this lesson the hard way when a clinical redesign project that reduced LOS in psychiatry failed to reduce year-one labor costs. A number of clinical leaders were not appropriately involved in the redesign efforts, and the hospital was not able to adjust staffing patterns to match the clinical change. This was a major learning experience for Yale-New Haven's leaders, who realized the importance of timely communication and the involvement of all departments contributing to the successful care of patients.

Today, Yale-New Haven involves nurse managers and department leaders earlier in the redesign journey and provides them with the meaningful data they need to manage their units and patients more effectively. For example, the finance team has automated a process that runs each unit's budgeted expenses through a costing system to create a budgeted cost per product or service, which can be compared with actual costs on a bi-weekly basis.

For years, Yale-New Haven has used a flex-budgeting process to match volumes to budget, adjusted for case mix changes. If volume on a nursing unit increases, the budget increases as well. If volume decreases, so does the unit's budget. However, leaders recognized that managers needed a better way to translate changes in volume to staffing changes. To that end, analysts in the finance department created a tool, called the payroll trend report, to help managers determine whether they are meeting their staffing per unit of service goals for their cost center, trended over time.

> *The finance team has automated a process that runs each unit's budgeted expenses through a costing system to create a budgeted cost per product or service, which can be compared with actual costs on a bi-weekly basis.*

The tool includes benchmark data, such as targeted worked hours per unit of service, as well as budgeted data and actual worked hours. The color-coded report allows nursing and clinical leaders to quickly determine where they are managing above target and below target. Each pay period, every cost center receives its own report, which pulls volume data from the EHR and cost data from the cost accounting system.

These integrated data allow department managers access to specific patient population trends over time, including shifts in quality outcomes. By clarifying for clinical and finance leaders the ways quality drives cost, the patient population quality trended data play a critical role in helping both parties understand past expense variation while working together to plan appropriately for future resource needs.

Bending the Cost Curve

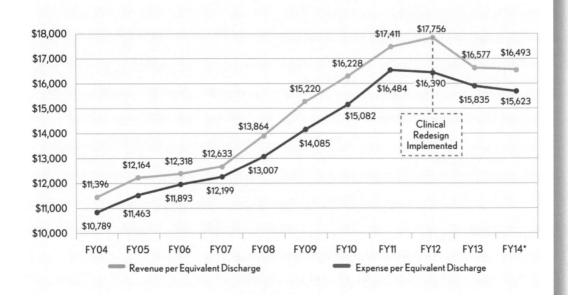

Prepare for bundled payments

As bundled payments become more of a reality, health systems need to test new technologies and processes to help them prepare for the journey from volume to value.

To prepare for bundled payments, finance leaders at Yale-New Haven are completing the rollout of a new data warehouse and analytics tool that will generate a more accurate cost of an episode of care, thereby providing more accurate utilization and cost data across the continuum of care so clinical leaders can more effectively manage their business in a bundled payment environment. For example, clinical and finance leaders in orthopedics are evaluating the quality and cost benefits of keeping patients undergoing hip replacements a

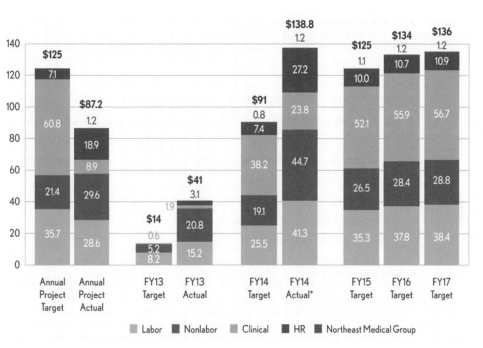

Savings Achieved at Yale-New Haven Health System

few days longer in the acute care setting, thereby avoiding admissions to skilled nursing facilities, and instead, discharging patients directly home with home health services. Although this process-of-care change increases the acute care cost, it potentially lowers the overall episode cost while also bringing a strong focus on improving patients' overall functional outcomes.

Yale-New Haven began participating in 11 bundled arrangements through the Centers for Medicare and Medicaid Services' Bundled Payments for Care Improvement initiative. Clinical and finance leaders at the system are actively tracking QVIs and other metrics, such as LOS in skilled nursing settings and readmissions, to identify process changes that can help reduce episode costs while, maintaining or improving quality.

The finance team is also implementing its cost accounting application in the system's physician practices to track productivity and clinical effectiveness measures, which will create a more accurate view of cost per case for the entire episode of care.

As more organizations like Yale-New Haven take on bundled payment arrangements, a greater percentage of their revenue will depend on quality outcomes. In such an environment, accurate cost accounting data are critical. Balcezak says: "Once you have that data, you can use it to forge relationships between people in finance who understand how care is paid for and the clinicians who ultimately drive the care." In this way, reducing inappropriate clinical variation can become the common ground for two camps that are still learning how to work together effectively to deliver better outcomes for patients and payers alike.

4.2

Using Cost Accounting Systems to Prepare for Value-Based Care

By Dan Michelson

UNDERSTAND THE TOTAL COST OF CARE TO DELIVER VALUE

Health systems are capitalizing on their cost accounting systems to reduce practice variation, tackle strategic initiatives and break even on Medicare.

In an industry long wedded to fee-for-service payment structures, understanding the true cost of an episode of care across multiple settings is rare. However, several organizations are tapping into their cost accounting systems to discern the total cost of care and prepare for a future defined by value-based payment.

Modeling physician performance

Until recently, only the flagship hospital at Mission Health, a five-hospital health system based in Asheville, NC, had a cost accounting system in place. "You would think cost accounting would be a core competency for any business, but small rural hospitals are there for the community first," says Larry Hill, vice president of finance. "As far as real performance detail goes, it is invisible."

To get a better handle on its performance, Mission is in the early stages of deploying a standardized cost accounting system across its facilities. The new system will accept data feeds from various clinical, supply chain and billing systems, and provide analytics that show how aggregate patient-level costs affect service line performance. Hill's goal is to build a dashboard-accessible financial planning tool in which local hospitals can set budgets, track performance, monitor physician cost drivers, and apply those data to proposed payer contracts down the line – contracts that will likely include more pay-for-performance measures.

One of Hill's first projects involves modeling physician performance. The health system has approximately 250 employed physicians whose compensation is based on work relative value units (RVUs), a standard of physician output that weighs the complexity of various tasks. Using a dashboard, Mission will present physicians with data on revenue generated by physician activity, associated costs and overall clinic performance across facilities. "If there is more transparency, physicians can understand how they affect cost," Hill says.

The finance executive is optimistic that a service line orientation – in which local departments can see how they are performing versus their peers in other facilities and adjust operations when needed – will catch on across Mission Health. "We can't get data fast enough. There is such a thirst for it," Hill says. "As we look at managing populations, we can better know who the population is at each facility and what that looks like financially."

Helping staff be strategic

Leaders at Legacy Health, a five-hospital, 1,500-bed delivery system in Portland, OR, know firsthand that analyzing the financial health of various service lines is a complicated undertaking. For one thing, it requires freeing up finance department staff from the tedious task of generating reports off legacy systems. For years, Legacy Health relied on a cumbersome system to produce reports of often dubious value, says Ben Shah, information systems director of enterprise systems and services. "We were just running numbers, not adding value," Shah says. "We were running more than 200 reports, many with the same data."

Shah spearheaded an effort to streamline the operation, not only discarding needless reports but also creating a dashboard where department leaders could parse their own financial summaries. Now the dashboard includes standard metrics such as discharges, service line percentages of volume and margin, revenue by payer, and revenue and labor benchmarks such as charity care and paid FTEs. Executives retrieve data electronically instead of combing through paper packets associated with legacy reports. Automating the reports has freed up considerable staff time. "We have reduced the number of FTEs working on financial decision support projects from eight to five," Shah says. "Now these employees are involved with other strategic initiatives that are helping us move forward."

> *"We have reduced the number of FTEs working on financial decision support projects from eight to five," Shah says. "Now these employees are involved with other strategic initiatives that are helping us move forward."*

For example, Shah recently completed a major analysis of a wide variance in operating room (OR) supply costs. Costs had spiked, but increased volume was not the cause. Using analytics tools in the cost accounting system, Shah's team undertook an in-depth analysis of OR performance, looking at payer mix, types of surgery, patient mix and service site. The group analyzed ORs by location and took into account many of the variables that drive costs, including physicians, patient diagnoses and complications. Shah's team eventually identified one physician who was a cost outlier because he was performing certain procedures in the cath lab, rather than the standard OR suite, where costs and personnel were lower.

That sole physician did not account for the entire spike in OR costs, but Shah says the exercise was useful in identifying how even one provider can cause a disproportionate rise. Shah's group later analyzed the use of implants and determined that newer physicians were coming on board and using more expensive implants. As a result, Legacy was able to shift its purchasing strategy and narrow its implants to a standard list to secure better pricing from vendors.

Legacy also is using cost accounting data to promote financial stewardship among its physicians. In the works is a "cost accounting 101" class targeting hospitalists. As part of the effort, the health system will provide data showing how hospitalist decisions ultimately drive the cost equation. "We can show how their costs vary from each other, including tests, imaging services and lab work," Shah says. "For example, do hospitalists really need to do a blood draw every hour? We can show the impact of those decisions, and then the hospitalists can look at the data from a clinical angle and challenge each other. We want to make sure what we are ordering is appropriate and we are not charging patients for things they don't need."

Of course, merely reducing expenses is not enough in the value-based care era, with many payer programs requiring providers to hit quality targets to qualify for shared savings or pay-for-performance bonuses. This dynamic underscores why leaders such as Shah use the cost accounting data as a starting point for discussions with the medical staff. Any changes in medical protocols are driven by physicians, not finance executives. "My job is to analyze," he says. "The data get us to that point, but then we turn it over to the clinical leadership."

Breaking even on Medicare

Health systems with large Medicare populations face some of the greatest financial challenges under healthcare reform. One example is Parrish Medical Center, a 250-bed acute care hospital in Titusville, FL, where approximately 55 percent of patients are insured by Medicare, says Mike Sitowitz, controller.

Parrish is embarking on a "Medicare break-even" analysis that the controller hopes will shine a light on previously obscure areas of operation. The hospital is analyzing the profitability of four main service lines – cardiology, neurosciences, orthopedics and pulmonology – under Medicare.

Using a cost accounting system, Sitowitz can drill down to the patient level to spot variations in treatment. Because the hospital has standard protocols and clinical pathways for treating certain ailments, the cost accounting system offers insight into instances when care varies from the path – instances that represent an opportunity to reduce waste and cut costs. The setup includes dashboards tailored to teams of physicians, who can compare themselves to their peers and see how they are working to help cut costs.

Sitowitz envisions turning over the dashboards to service line leaders, who can make inferences for the future using the cost accounting data and the system's forecasting tools. "We will need to operate with less reimbursement and get our costs in line," says Sitowitz, offering a pithy summation of the industry's future – and of why cost accounting is here to stay.

EMPLOY A SERVICE LINE MANAGEMENT STRUCTURE

4.3

Setting a Course for Growth through Optimal Service Line Performance

By Jennifer Ittner and Alina Henderson

Setting a course for growth in the age of value-based care requires providers to have planning agility, visibility into performance, and a leadership structure that is in sync with the organization's goals.

Healthcare systems must align the way they track and manage performance with the way they deliver care and how they are reimbursed for that care under value-based payment models. This is a complex challenge—not only because the provider takes on more of the financial risk of providing care but also because this requires using an entirely new lens through which to assess the performance of the organization. It is increasingly important for providers to understand and manage the cost of care related to episodes versus encounters.

One of the key ways to succeed under these new payment models is employing a management structure that is conducive to the measurement and improvement of episodic cost and quality. This means, at minimum, the organization's data must be organized in such a way to achieve an understanding of costs across departments and the entire continuum of care for a specific service line. Ideally, the organization's leadership structure will also reflect these defined service lines. Managing cost and quality data within defined service lines, addressing performance gaps with clear accountability, and planning based on service-line projections are key success factors for growth.

Service line dyad management, which pairs a clinician and administrator to manage the operations of a clinical area across a health system, has also become increasingly important for quality improvement and driving organizational growth. The dyad model must be supported by data analytics that provide a foundation for improvement, service line reporting, and a strong organizational infrastructure that fosters continued improvement and success.

Key benefits

The service line structure is organized along the patient's continuum of care as opposed to the organization's department structure. This brings cross departmental leadership and staff together to manage similar patient populations and align better with the patient's experience. This approach to managing clinical services allows for a more efficient allocation of organizational resources, such as staff and capital, and enables an organization to assess vulnerable areas and adjust to market forces more quickly.

When designed and implemented appropriately, service line management can more effectively reduce both clinical and operational costs associated with managing a population of patients—which is essential for capturing value-based revenue and improving margins. At the same time, service line management can also lead to reduced clinical variation and improved care coordination, which results in better quality. By reducing costs and improving quality, the organization is positioned for growth through improved margins and increased market share.

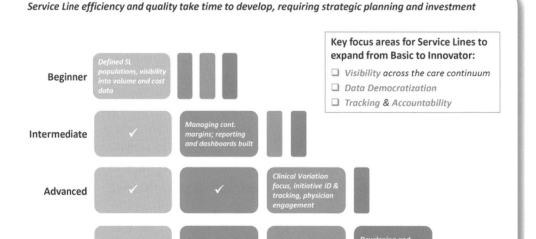

Evolution of Service Lines

Service Line efficiency and quality take time to develop, requiring strategic planning and investment

Evolution of the service line

Although approaches differ, fundamentally service line management represents a cultural and tactical shift that, in addition to strategic planning and investment, requires leadership buy-in across clinical, financial, and operational departments.

Effective service line management also takes time to mature, evolving in stages defined by progressive capabilities starting with beginner and growing to intermediate, advanced, and innovator.

The foundation of the service line management approach is service line analytics— data that is accessed, analyzed, and reported upon for a specific patient population. Once service lines are clearly defined, a structured analytics strategy will ensure that stakeholders are receiving consistent and accurate data to drive action. These analytics are used to identify the cost and profitability of service lines. This is the first step into understanding areas of opportunity for growth and areas of waste and inefficiency within the care delivery system.

The following stages describe key capabilities in employing analytics along the evolution of service line management along with the various software tools that can make data analysis easier, provide more timely reporting, and ultimately, enable service line maturity and growth.

Beginner

Service line management starts with defining a patient population (e.g. cardiac patients) and working to improve access to the data and end user acceptance and validation of the data. The data should be considered a part of routine decision making and not a one-time report. The data should be easily updated, flexible, and reviewed frequently by operations and leadership. Weaving this data into day to day operations begins to provide visibility into service line analytics and helps the organization build a foundation to support additional service line growth.

Tools: Decision support service lines. These tools encompass software that allows for defining service lines and has the flexibility to leverage MS-DRGs, ICD codes, or other patient defining characteristics such as age, payor group, and clinical test results that assist with cohorting patients for additional analysis.

In 2016, the CEO of a three hospital system in Texas outlined a strategic goal to transition the way the organization analyzes and manages its performance from a department model to a service line model. Leadership tasked Finance with defining the service lines and communicating the new approach across the organization. To ensure a committed focus on this goal, the CFO established a team of leaders from operations, marketing, strategy, and clinical areas, with goals to educate stakeholders and determine the most appropriate service line categories. The cross-functional team developed a plan to communicate the new model to stakeholders across the organization, focusing on the value and benefits of a service line strategy. To select and validate service line categories, the Finance team was responsible for running analysis while the cross-functional team addressed common categorization questions (e.g. whether transplants should be organized by MS-DRGs or ICD codes). Once the service lines were clearly defined, the information was socialized with the rest of the organization and the team held additional communication sessions to ensure all necessary groups understood the new structure. The service line definitions were then loaded into the organization's Decision Support tool and leadership immediately began tracking volumes by service line.

Intermediate

The next step is gaining visibility into volumes and financial performance data. Tracking basic cost data (labor, supplies, ancillary services, etc.), measuring contribution margin, incorporating quality measures into the analytics, and developing reports and dashboards for various stakeholder audiences are key to having intermediate proficiency.

Tools: Decision Support costing and dashboards. These tools integrate data from clinical and operational areas and provide visibility into basic cost data for a patient population. Decision support is critical for service line maturity as it provides visibility into sources of cost variation and unfavorable financial performance. Tools that measure quality can be added to decision support software to identify adverse events that occur during the inpatient stay. This data should then be compared to readmission data to assist providers with prioritizing quality improvement initiatives.

For example, analysis on acute myocardial infarction and coronary artery bypass graft patients will present pertinent data for an episode of care, such as total costs, direct costs, net revenue, and expected payment for all visits that occur during the 90-day episode. This data is then used to calculate the contribution margin and operating margin for the service line and analyze trends in readmissions.

A community health system in Illinois has been leveraging their Decision Support system to set up financial performance tracking at the service line level and incorporate quality outcomes into their analysis. The finance team has been partnering with clinical and operational leadership to develop cost and quality dashboards. This exercise has led to a review and education of how costs are calculated and what are the inputs that drive cost. Clinical and operations leadership now have more visibility into service line margins and revenue. Incorporating quality data into the financial dashboards have also provided new insight into how adverse events affect length of stay, readmissions, costs and the service lines' bottom line. Finance is now meeting regularly with operational and clinical stakeholders to review the data and begin discussing performance goals. Once the goals are set up, a regular meeting cadence will be established to review the dashboards, service line performance, trends and report variances to the goal.

> *A community health system in Illinois has been leveraging their Decision Support system to set up financial performance tracking at the service line level and incorporate quality outcomes into their analysis.*

Quality Variation Impact on Cost Per Case

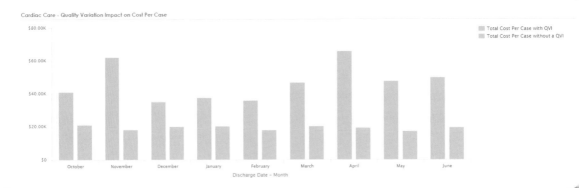

Advanced

At this step, data analytics are actionable. The data is being used to identify ways to reduce costs and improve quality. Opportunities for cost reduction and quality improvement are implemented and tracked monthly with physician and executive engagement. This is important as organizations begin to shift from fee for service to fee for value. In fee for value payment arrangements, the only way to increase an organization's profitability is to reduce the cost of care. Organizations that have a culture of continuous improvement and see the reduction of cost and waste as an ongoing priority will be better set up for future growth.

Tool: Continuous improvement or project management tools. Mature service line management combines the use of decision support tools with process improvement solutions to identify cost savings opportunities, prioritize the opportunities, provide drill down analytics into the data, and then track improvements over time. This allows users to spend less time analyzing data and more time driving organizational change.

Continuous improvement tools, used at different levels at the intermediate and advanced stages, review multiple types of

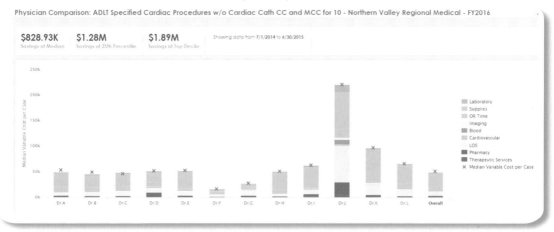

Physician Comparison

Physician Comparison: ADLT Specified Cardiac Procedures w/o Cardiac Cath CC and MCC for 10 - Northern Valley Regional Medical - FY2016

data including general ledger, cost accounting, patient charges, diagnosis codes, contracted rates and reimbursement, supply acquisition costs, payroll, time and attendance, and admission/discharge/transfer data in order to identify and prioritize savings opportunities. Through algorithms and workflow, the toolset should enable a process and accountability structure for improvement. The toolset will assist in identifying, evaluating, prioritizing, and planning cost saving initiatives, as well as track progress at the initiative and organizational goal levels.

A more sophisticated tool will analyze cost accounting data in areas such as supplies, pharmacy, ancillary services and length of stay to detect differences in care delivery patterns that lead to unnecessary variation in care and cost. The tool should allow users to drill down into these variations in utilization, such as supply usage by provider, and compare provider costs against the median supply cost per case. The tool should facilitate conversations by providers on how to better manage the cost of care without affecting the quality of care.

Continuous improvement tools reduce the time spent on the "heavy lifting" of analytics required to identify opportunities and track progress. This allows for more time to be spent driving action to reduce costs and improve quality.

A community hospital in the Northeast has implemented a Continuous Improvement tool on top of their Decision Support tool. This new functionality has identified cost reduction opportunities that total 5 percent of the hospital's annual operating expense. The organization has a goal to reduce their costs over the next several years and finance has begun partnering with clinical leadership to investigate the opportunities found by the continuous improvement tool, set up cost reduction goals, and begin to tracking performance against these goals. Each service line's cost reduction opportunity that was identified by the system was assigned a project manager/owner within the Performance Improvement Group to analyze the data underlying the opportunity and meet with clinical and operational leadership to set up a cost reduction goal for the fiscal year. The finance owner and the clinical leader then met with clinical stakeholders together to review the data, obtain feedback, and discuss how the goal will be measured for the upcoming fiscal year. Monthly progress towards the goal is then reviewed at the project level, service line level, and leadership level. At the leadership level, the organization reviews overall progress towards the annual goal, which projects are not tracking towards their goal, the reasons behind the variance, and how can they assist with getting the project back on track. Goal alignment at the leadership level and physician engagement is critical to the success of this program.

The finance owner and the clinical leader met with clinical stakeholders together to review the data, obtain feedback, and discuss how the goal will be measured for the upcoming fiscal year.

The cost reduction goal is a year over year goal. Therefore, the hospital is currently preparing to review system-identified cost savings opportunities for FY19. Cost savings opportunities will be reviewed during the budget planning process to assist with the closing of budget gaps. Improvement goals will be incorporated into the budget and will assist with FY19 goal alignment. It is important to have systems that have automated tracking capabilities so that previous fiscal year improvement efforts can continue to be tracked along with new initiatives so that the risk of backsliding on improvement gains is reduced or at minimum is easily identified so that project teams can be mobilized for course correction.

Innovator

At the innovator stage, with a clear line of sight into margin and quality data, as well as a structure to improve on those metrics, providers should be able to assess and define patient populations that qualify (low variance, high volume) for risk-based contracts with commercial payers.

Tool: Episode grouper. Tools that enable analyzing which encounters should be in/out of scope for bundles will assist with setting up a value based program that is beneficial to both the provider and the payer.

In early 2016, a group of physicians at a cancer center in the Midwest who were closely engaged with their service lines' performance and strategy, realized they were uniquely positioned in the marketplace to deliver more world-class care and improve margins. They were interested in proposing bundled services to their commercial payers however they did not have the technology to support this goal. They needed a tool that would analyze current volumes, quality and cost data to ensure they were developing bundled populations that would achieve their target metrics. They partnered to develop a tool that would allow them to analyze episodes and create specific patient populations with which to do scenario modeling and understand optimal episodes of care which could benefit their patients and their organization. The new functionality has allowed them to identify, adjust and track patient populations over a span of time and allow them to begin negotiating with payers on new and innovating payment models. Supporting Infrastructure

Beyond the analytics and tools, effective service line management is dependent upon a strong organizational infrastructure that supports planning, performance management, and process improvement initiatives within service lines.

Keys components of this infrastructure include:

Leadership buy-in. An essential element in any improvement initiative is buy-in and support from clinical, operational, and financial leadership. Leadership must understand the scope of the service line priorities, be committed to the same goals, rally support amongst its teams, and drive accountability at all levels of the organization.

Dedicated team. Tools can identify opportunities, set targets, and prioritize work—but they cannot drive change. This requires the work of dedicated individuals that can manage a cross-functional project team to deliver results. Project managers should be able to focus solely (75 percent of their time, at minimum) on the process improvement initiatives. Managers who are juggling these tasks with other work will find it challenging to carve out time from their daily operational duties to achieve results.

Change methodology. Part of the supporting structure is a methodology for change. This may include such process improvement approaches as Lean, Six Sigma or PDSA (plan-do-study-act). Coalescing around one approach to problem solving will provide structure and a common language for project teams. It will also help leadership to understand how a project runs and make change more comfortable. Change is hard; having a routine/methodology for change helps weave process improvement into an organization's culture and makes change less scary.

Continuous reporting. Finally, one of the challenges with performance improvement initiatives is how to sustain progress once the project has been completed. If data is not updated and revisited continuously, there is a risk of backsliding and losing the gains that were achieved by the project team. A core benefit of a continuous improvement platform is that it automates reporting, which can be the key to sustainability. Performance data must be presented to stakeholders regularly in a concise and easily accessible manner. If their work is effective, the data will reflect that success; if not, the need for other approaches will be readily apparent and allow for faster course correction to sustain improvement gains. Continuous, automatic data reporting makes it easier to track progress and sustain results.

Preparing for growth

Service line management driven by analytics and sophisticated tools enables healthcare leaders to better steer their businesses to success in a continuously changing environment. At the same time, an infrastructure of strong leadership, dedicated management and oversight, and process improvement will help lead to sustainable success.

Republished, with permission, from the March 2018 issue of hfm.
Three Westbrook Corporate Center, Suite 600, Westchester, IL 60154-5732.
For more information, call 800-252-HFMA or vist hfma.org

SUSTAIN
OPERATING
MARGIN

4.4

Sustaining Operating Margin in CJR Cases: A Recipe for Financial Success

By Liz Kirk

To achieve financial success under the CJR model and under the many innovative value-based payment models that will follow, most health systems must make a quantum leap in their sophistication of cost accounting and data analytics capabilities.

Although the Comprehensive Care for Joint Replacement (CJR) model is officially underway, many health systems—large and small, academic and community focused—lack the tools, data, and accountability structure necessary to succeed under its new payment rules.

Hip and knee replacements represent a sizable portion of surgical volume for many hospitals with a high Medicare population. Moreover, these procedures have high costs ($14,000-$25,000) and payment ($23,000-$27,000) under Medicare compared with other high-volume procedures. Simply put, these cases contribute disproportionately to revenue and cost. Even a small decline in revenue and margin for these cases will produce a noticeable impact on an organization's overall operating margin.

The recipe for financial success under the CJR model includes having trusted and accessible cost and clinical data at a physician- and patient-specific level. But simply having the data is not enough; an organization must be able to effectively use these data to compel action and sustain improvements, and it must do so with a primary emphasis on preventing harm.

Create a system for effective Cost Accounting

Advanced cost accounting systems are essential for producing the type of information required for success under the CJR model. An advanced cost accounting system will do much more than allocate overhead costs to charge codes and do the math for cost-to-charge ratio (CCR) cost estimates. State-of-the-art cost accounting systems enable patient-level costing based on acuity, actual supply cost, actual drug cost, actual staffing cost, and time required to deliver the services. Moreover, and especially important for the CJR model, by incorporating claims data, an advanced cost accounting systems will enable users to access cost and clinical data not only from the acute care setting but also from across the continuum of care for entities in and outside of the health system.

Once an organization has access to cost data that are specific and broad, it can begin to analyze these data in combination with clinical, quality, satisfaction, and outcomes data to gain insight into what actions can be taken to reduce acute care costs, improve quality, select the appropriate post-acute setting, and more. At one time, performing such a data analysis was a laborious—even daunting—process, requiring significant time and effort to pull data together from independent information systems that, in many cases, were owned by different departments throughout a hospital. Often, the only tool analysts had at their disposal was an Excel file.

The situation has improved dramatically in recent years, with the emergence of advanced cost accounting tools that combine data across the continuum, enable nimble access to broad data, and provide intuitive interfaces for end users to run analysis. With such tools, it now is possible for hospitals and health systems to dive into clinical and quality variation, which are significant factors that influence operating margin on CJR cases.

Use the data to drive action

With the combination of clinical and cost data as a foundation, organizations now can not only identify variation in care decisions at the patient and physician levels, but also, more important, quantify the financial impact of such variation. In fact, findings of recent analyses of inpatient cases for eight major health systems suggest that clinical variation accounts for 2 to 4 percent of an organization's operating expense. This variation is reflected in utilization decisions, such as implant selection and length of stay (LOS), and in treatment decisions, such as chemo prophylaxis to prevent deep vein thrombosis and pulmonary embolisms (DVT/PE), which can help reduce the incidence of hospital-acquired conditions (HACs). As more case rate and bundled payments take effect, organizations will need to minimize such variation to be able to sustain and improve margin.

Consider the example of an organization that performs 300 total knee replacements annually. The CJR payment per case is $23,000. For simplicity, those 300 cases are equally split among three physicians. By accessing combined clinical and cost data, we know that the physicians' direct variable inpatient cost per case varies, primarily because of variation in length of stay (LOS) and implant selection. As the exhibit below shows, physician A, on average, returns a negative margin on each case, resulting in a cost to the hospital of $200,000 per year.

Comparative Data for 3 Physicians on Knee Replacement Costs per Case

	Cases	Total Inpatient Cost	Average Length of Stay	Average Room and Board Cost/Case	Implant Cost	Reimbursement per Case	Margin per Case	Annual Profit/Loss
COMPARATIVE DATA FOR 3 PHYSICIANS ON KNEE REPLACEMENT COSTS PER CASE								
Physician A	100	$25,000	6	$4,800	$11,500	$23,000	($2,000)	($200,000)
Physician B	100	$20,000	3	$2,400	$8,500	$23,000	$3,000	$300,000
Physician C	100	$21,000	4	$1,800	$7,500	$23,000	$2,000	$200,000

Published in hfm Early Edition, August 2016 (hfma.org/hfm)

Before changing clinical decisions, physicians typically want to see the acuity of their cases, the age distribution of their patients, and key quality indicators, such as HACs and readmissions, compared with the same measures for their higher and lower cost peers. Providing such comparative insight is important because it either validates or invalidates the need for the variance in practice, and it ensures that care decisions remain under the control of the physician.

Extending beyond the hospital, making the discharge disposition of patients transparent and the cost of common discharge decisions available to physicians is essential for influencing the cost of care beyond the inpatient setting.

For example, the exhibit below shows physician A has an older patient population but—as shown in the previous exhibit—is consistently selecting a high-end implant. The physician also is frequently discharging patients to a skilled nursing facility (SNF) despite having severity of illness and risk of mortality percentages that are lower than those for physician C. Physician A's quality of care is not higher despite higher cost, as demonstrated by the percentage of cases that are readmitted and those that have HACs.

Comparative Data for 3 Physicians on Knee Replacement Quality Indicators

	Cases	Average Age	Percentage of Cases with Severity of Illness of 3 or 4	Percentage of Cases with Risk of Mortality 3 or 4	Percentage of Cases with Hospital-Acquired Conditions	Percentage of Cases with Related 90-Day Readmission	Average Length of Stay	Mode Discharge Disposition
Physician A	100	71.3	3%	5%	5%	10%	6	SNF
Physician B	100	64	2%	4%	3%	7%	3	Home Health
Physician C	100	71	5%	7%	1%	2%	4	Home

Published in hfm Early Edition, August 2016 (hfma.org/hfm).

The cost of care for the inpatient event and the post-acute care is much higher, as shown in the exhibit below. Under CJR reimbursement, this physician will cost the health system hundreds of thousands dollars each year.

Comparative Data for 3 Physicians on Knee Replacement: Total Episode Costs and Implant Costs

COMPARATIVE DATA FOR 3 PHYSICIANS ON KNEE REPLACEMENT: TOTAL EPISODE COSTS AND IMPLANT COSTS					
	Cases	Total Inpatient Cost	Average Post-Acute Care Cost	Total Episode Cost of Care	Implant Cost
Physician A	100	$25,000	$12,000	$37,000	$11,500
Physician B	100	$20,000	$6,000	$26,000	$8,500
Physician C	100	$21,000	$1,500	$22,500	$7,500

Published in *hfm Early Edition*, August 2016 (hfma.org/hfm).

Engage physicians in the process

Even with sophisticated tools that make it possible to obtain this type of actionable information, the task is far from complete. Once the analyses have been performed and the information is available and shared with physicians, organizational leadership (often the chief medical officer or chief quality officer) needs to step in to pave the way for the physicians to consider lower cost care decisions. Various actions can be taken to promote physician engagement, including:

- Providing clinically validated studies showing comparable clinical efficacy and risk

- Paying for physicians to receive training on lower cost devices and implants

- Instituting gainsharing with physicians on savings

- Collaborating with the physicians to create a standard care plan

- Providing physicians with physician assistants or advanced practice nurses to ensure care progresses while patients are in inpatient units and physicians are in surgery or clinic

Take steps to avoid preventable harm

If they aren't already, facilities participating in the CJR model should be obsessively focused on clinical quality and HACs and patient safety incidents (PSIs). Only recently, a few leading health systems have been able to quantify the cost of preventable harm—and the numbers are astounding. Cases with HACs and PSIs cost three to four times the median cost per case without quality issues. Yale New Haven Health System, for example, saved more than $150 million by reducing the incidence of what it calls Quality Variation Indicators™ (QVIs), a proprietary measure representing all in-hospital harm.

Under the CJR model, a hospital's target payment for the inpatient event, in year one, and for the episode of care through 90 days post-discharge, in years two through five, is reduced 1.5 to 3 percent based on the organization's composite quality score from the 2012 through 2014 federal fiscal years. For an organization that performs 1,000 total hip and knee replacements per year within Medicare, the approximate range of this reduction in aggregate Medicare reimbursement is from $350,000 to $800,000. Over the five years of the demonstration program, the quality composite scores are recalculated to reflect more recent years. The deduction amount can change, so focusing on reducing the number of cases with HACs and PSIs will decrease the amount of the quality deductions in the later years. As the population ages, case volume increases, and similar programs expand, minimizing the quality deduction impact on revenue is essential.

However, the more significant impact on payment will come from the individual cases that experience HACs and PSIs. Under the CJR payment structure, organizations have stop-loss and stop-gain provisions that have limits, unlike typical outlier payments.

To understand the impact, let's consider our hospital that performs 1,000 total hip and knee replacement cases per year.

For cases without HACs or PSIs, the median total cost per case is $20,000. This median cost works out well for the hospital because the Medicare payment is $23,000. The median operating margin per case is $3,000 (15%).

But if a patient experiences an HAC or a PSI, the cost will likely be three to four times the median, say $70,000. The DRG would likely be upgraded to DRG 469 (major joint replacement or reattachment of lower extremity with major complications or comorbidities) to reflect the complications. DRG 469 reimburses $50,000, on average, plus the CJR stop-loss adjustment, which in years two through five is 20 percent of the target payment, or $4,600. So the case that costs $70,000 is now reimbursed at $54,600, representing a $15,400 loss and –22 percent operating margin. If the HAC and PSI rate is 7 percent for all total hip and knee replacements performed at this organization, and each one has similar economics to the one above, the organization will lose more than $1,000,000 on these cases.

The cost of harm adds up quickly. And as the CJR model continues, the penalties and the downside risk only go up. Under such circumstances, a healthcare provider can't afford not to be focused on delivering high-quality care.

4.5

Driving Savings While

Improving Outcomes

By Laura Ramos Hegwer

IMPROVE
ACROSS THE
CONTINUUM

Today, more than two-thirds of hospitals with 50 beds or more have palliative care programs (Dumanovsky, T., Rachel, A., Rogers, M., et al., "The Growth of Palliative Care in U.S. Hospitals: A Status Report," *Journal of Palliative Medicine*, Dec. 24, 2015.) In this interview, Vincent M. Obi, CPA , director, decision support, Virginia Hospital Center, Arlington, Va., offers strategies for hospitals to measure the value of their palliative care programs.

On the impetus for finding value.

In 2005, a recently hired physician and a nurse clinical coordinator began to offer palliative care at Virginia Hospital Center, a 334-bed, not-for-profit teaching hospital. Their goal was to provide better end-of-life care to patients with cancer, chronic obstructive pulmonary disease (COPD), and other conditions. The physician asked Obi and his team if they could help him prove that palliative care reduced costs and improved care to justify the investment in FTEs.

"As an acute care hospital, we get paid either a DRG case rate or a per diem, so there is no additional reimbursement for adding the staff," says Obi. "So we truly had to show that the new service would improve cost savings and the quality of care."

Obi leads the hospital's decision support team, which includes two analysts. He also shares a business intelligence data warehouse architect who reports to IT. Obi's team is responsible for cost accounting, contract modeling, and assessing profitability by service lines. The team also assists with some clinical reporting.

On providing palliative services via consult.

Some hospitals maintain a separate palliative care unit, which charges a room-and- board charge. This makes it easier to track and associate the cost of palliative care to a case, Obi says. But other organizations like Virginia Hospital Center do not have a separate palliative care unit and instead provide palliative services via consult. In such a model, palliative care cases can be located on any floor, and the palliative care team travels to the patient. A member of the care team may call the palliative care nurse or social worker to assess whether the patient is a candidate for palliative care services. Patients and family members also can request a consult with a member of the palliative care team.

Without a room-and-board charge, the decision support team has a more difficult time tracking the cost of these cases. "We depend on medical records to code those cases properly," Obi says. In addition, overhead costs are allocated to the floors.

On determining the cost savings.

Obi and his team set out to measure days and costs saved using their decision support system. To do this, they selected palliative care cases by DRG. Then, they created a patient population with these DRGs and selected non-palliative cases with the same DRGs. When they created a report comparing the average length of stay (ALOS) for these two populations, they found that the overall palliative care ALOS was consistently lower for the palliative care cases. Specifically, palliative care saved more than nine days in LOS per case. In 2016, palliative care saved a total 5,099 days.

Using the difference between the ALOS, Obi and his team could calculate total days saved based on cases that did receive palliative

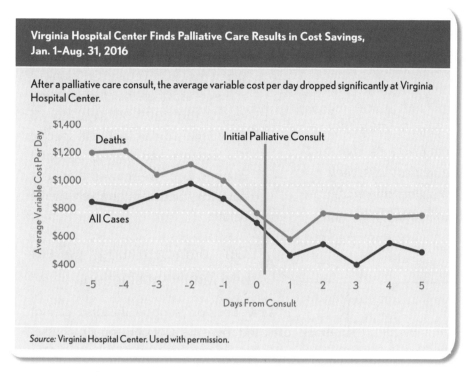

Virginia Hospital Center Finds Palliative Care Results in Cost Savings, Jan. 1–Aug. 31, 2016

After a palliative care consult, the average variable cost per day dropped significantly at Virginia Hospital Center.

Source: Virginia Hospital Center. Used with permission.

care. In 2016, their total variable cost savings, including labor, amounted to $3.7 million. Then, they calculated the variable cost savings without labor. "Our theory was that we would not lay off staff, but move them to another service." By focusing mainly on supplies and pharmaceuticals, they could arrive at a more conservative cost savings, nearly $1.7 million in 2016.

The DRG associated with the greatest cost savings was 871 for septicemia or severe sepsis. Palliative care for these patients saved 356 days in 2016, leading to more than $117,000 in cost savings.

Obi and his team also wanted to measure cost savings achieved by using less interventional care and more palliative care. To do this, they developed a consult date field in their decision support system, which is based on the first consult date in their electronic health record. Then, they measured the average variable cost savings per day before and after the consult. From there, they compared the average cost savings by department summary so they could understand where the cost savings originated.

Areas associated with significant costs savings included room and board, ICU, pharmacy, and supplies. "When the CEO, CFO, and CNO looked at the cost savings, their first question was, 'Is this real?'" Obi says. "So we added more detail, looked at specific ICU patients, and analyzed detailed charges. Once we showed them this data, they were comfortable with the results."

> *"When the CEO, CFO, and CNO looked at the cost savings, their first question was, 'Is this real?'" Obi says.*

On demonstrating patient and family satisfaction.

"Many decision support systems cannot track costs, and there are a lot of manual processes involved in tracking these cases," Obi says. One of the challenges was determining the first consult date. "We depend on the coders and system to make sure it is reported properly, which is an evolving process."

Today, Virginia Hospital Center's palliative care team has grown to include two employed physicians, a coordinator, a nurse, a social worker, a chaplain, and bereavement staff. They also have a palliative care team from Kaiser Permanente that treats members at the hospital.

As the U.S. population ages, the need for palliative care will grow. Virginia Hospital Center's analysis has helped it meet the needs of its population, Obi says. "Palliative care can improve quality of care at the end of life," he says. "In finance, it's possible to make the case to upper management to allocate resources to these programs."

4.6

Improved Quality of Health Care Does Equate to Lower Costs

By Jennifer Ittner and Jami Eddington

Standard care protocols were observed to be effective in improving care quality and reducing cost in a study comparing quality and cost outcomes with and without the use of such protocols.

Over the past decade, hospitals have been implementing process and quality improvement programs using strategies proven in other industries to solve their complex challenges. A primary focus of these efforts has been to identify standard care protocols that can contribute not only to improved outcomes but also to reduced costs.

These efforts raise two important questions that should be of interest to finance leaders of hospitals and health systems:

What is the most effective methodology for identifying such standard care protocols?

What actual evidence exists to show that such protocols are actually effective in improving outcomes and reducing costs?

Improving care processes: The Lean approach

One methodology for identifying standard care protocols that has been widely adopted is lean. The Cambridge-Mass.-based

Lean Enterprise Institute describes lean as a system that seeks to increase value for customers with fewer resources by eliminating waste or steps that do not add value.

Lean changes thinking at the levels of both the organization and the individual. In lean, a reviewer examines every step in a process, asking whether the step is in any way valuable to the customer. If the step lacks any apparent value, the next question is whether it can be eliminated or—if eliminating it is not possible—whether the amount of time spent on it can be reduced. In a hospital setting, the customer is the patient.

Using lean to examine hospital processes provides a broader perspective than can be gained from simply looking at processes occurring in just one department. A lean reviewer follows every step that a patient encounters with the organization, looking at the patient's experiences across departments, specialties, and cross functional teams. A lean team then collaborates to redesign processes to make them more efficient (remove waste) and effective (add value).

The reviewer should be someone who is trained in lean. In a hospital, it could be someone in process improvement, quality, project management, or operations management. Team members would be any individuals who are involved in the steps in the process. If the process is making check-in more efficient, for example, then the team members should be from patient access and registration—ideally from the department where the change is occurring. If the process is focused on making changes to order sets, then the team should include clinical experts, physicians who will be entering orders, and other parties affected, such as representatives from pharmacy, nursing, and ancillary service areas.

Such a practice aligns with the intent of the Centers for Medicare & Medicaid Services (CMS) in advancing Medicare alternative payment models (APMs). CMS is developing programs in which hospitals are paid on the basis of the value of the care they deliver, rather than the volume of that care. The essential idea underlying the Comprehensive Care for Joint Replacement (CJR) model, for example, is to view a clinical episode from the patient's perspective. The CJR model is testing a way to bundle payment and quality measurement for an episode of care associated with hip and knee replacements with the larger goal of encouraging hospitals, physicians, and post-acute providers to work together to coordinate care and increase value. Hospitals also have an incentive to reduce patient complications (improve quality and value) and reduce costs (minimize waste) associated with the episode of care. Using lean practices, therefore, may offer one of the best means for hospitals to begin to grapple with managing such APMs.

> *By enabling physicians to find all orders needed for treatment in one place, standard order sets not only improve efficiency but also allow for best practices on clinical care pathways to be presented in an actionable way.*

As processes are viewed and revamped from a lean perspective, the new process developed should then be used consistently with every customer. The idea of promoting this level of standardization of work in health care may seem counter intuitive, given that it is the individual who is most valued in health care, with the inherent understanding that each patient is unique and has unique needs. Moreover, physicians are valued, first and foremost, for their ability to diagnose and treat each patient's unique symptoms and needs. Decision-making at the individual level therefore is important. Nonetheless, it also stands to reason that if a process is clearly identified as being the best, there is a sound rationale for adopting it as standard practice.

As was suggested previously, lean is a useful methodology in a hospital setting for the development of standard care protocols, including standard order sets. When developed with cross functional teams and clinical expertise, standard order sets identify the best way for a physician to treat a patient and minimize waste. By enabling physicians to find all orders needed for treatment in one place, instead of having to search for and sign single orders multiple times, standard order sets not only improve efficiency but also allow for best practices on clinical care pathways to be presented in an actionable way.

Case study: Effectiveness of standard order sets

Standard order sets have been widely touted as an effective means to improve patient outcomes and reduce costs for organizations. Until recently, however, that claim has been difficult to prove.

To assess the effectiveness of standard order sets and their impact on cost and quality, a study was performed examining compliance with core measures and standard order sets at a 1,000-bed hospital in the southeastern United States. This study's findings corroborate what has long been suspected: that standard treatment protocols do correlate with better patient outcomes and reduce waste (cost) for the organization.

The study reviewed core measure order set compliance for acute myocardial infarction (heart attack), heart failure, hemorrhagic stroke, pneumonia, sepsis, and stroke. Quality outcomes were assessed using Yale New Haven Health System's Quality Variation Indicators™ (QVI) methodology. QVIs are defined as potentially preventable adverse events occurring in inpatient encounters that, with the exception of surgical site infection, are not present on admission.

There are 28 QVI categories with 65 specific QVIs ranging from respiratory failure, to ventilator-associated pneumonia, to postoperative wound dehiscence.

QVI outcomes were used because they are more comprehensive than other outcome measures available, including the Agency for Healthcare Research and Quality (AHRQ) Patient Safety Indicators (PSIs). For example, AHRQ PSI 12 Perioperative Pulmonary Embolism (PE) or Deep Vein Thrombosis (DVT) Rate measures only PEs and DVTs affecting surgical inpatients. By contrast, the

Thrombosis QVI captures all PEs and DVTs occurring during an inpatient stay (surgical, medical, and obstetric).

YALE NEW HAVEN HEALTH SYSTEM QUALITY VARIATION INDICATORS™ CATEGORIES	
1. Complication of Procedure	15. Respiratory Failure
2. Complication Device/Implant/Graft	16. Shock
3. Foreign Object Retained	17. Infection: CAUTI
4. Perforation/Laceration	18. Infection: Vascular Catheter-associated
5. Transfusion Reaction	19. Infection
6. Iatrogenic Condition	20. Delirium
7. Falls/Trauma	21. Diabetes Complication
8. Pressure Ulcer	22. Post Op Wound Dehiscence
9. Thrombosis/Embolism	23. Obstetric Trauma
10. Air Embolism	24. Complication: Pregnancy/Birth
11. Pneumonia: Ventilator-associated	25. Malignant Hypertension
12. Pneumonia: Aspiration Post Procedure	26. Compartment Syndrome
13. Poisoning by Drugs	27. Allergic Reaction: Anaphylaxis
14. Complication: Post-Op Shock	28. Adverse Events

Source: Yale New Haven Health System

Published in hfm Early Edition, November 2016 (hfma.org/hfm).

The findings: Quality

The hospital identified nearly 9,000 inpatient encounters over a one-year period that qualified for the use of one or more of the core measure standard order sets. In actual practice, only 30 percent of these 9,000 (about 2,700 patients) received standard care protocols via an established treatment order set. The study found that, of the 9,000 patients, 14.5 percent (about 1,300 patients) had acquired one or more preventable adverse events (QVIs) during their inpatient visit.

When the patients were stratified, it was found that 16 percent of patients who did not receive the appropriate core measure order set acquired one or more QVIs, whereas only 11 percent of patients who received the appropriate core measure order set acquired one or more QVIs. This finding suggests a patient who is not treated using the appropriate core measure standard care protocol has a greater likelihood of acquiring one or more QVIs during an inpatient stay than a patient who undergoes this treatment protocol (p-value < 0.0001).

The findings: Cost

In examining costs for the same 9,000 patients, patients who did not receive treatment using the appropriate core measure standard care protocol incurred significantly more costs than did patients who received treatment under the appropriate core measure order set (p-value < 0.0001). The average direct variable cost per case for those patients whose treatment did not follow the standard care protocol was $11,140, compared with an average direct variable cost of $8,070 per case for patients whose treatment followed the protocol.

> *Among patients who experienced a QVI, costs of care for those whose treatment complied with the appropriate core measure order set were significantly lower than for those whose treatment did not follow the standard protocol.*

For patients who were treated under the appropriate order set, but still acquired a QVI, the average direct variable cost per case was $23,978, whereas for patients who were not treated under the appropriate order set and acquired a QVI, the average direct variable cost per case was $35,538. Thus, among patients who experienced a QVI, costs of care for those whose treatment complied with the appropriate core measure order set were significantly lower than for those whose treatment did not follow the standard protocol (p-value = 0.0008).

Sepsis: A closer look

The largest disparity between QVI rates, relative to order set compliance, was seen among patients qualifying for the sepsis core measure standard order set. Likewise, the largest discrepancies in average costs per case were seen among patients with sepsis.

The hospital identified nearly 2,200 inpatients qualifying for the sepsis core measure order set, of whom 31 percent received the appropriate order set. Of the 69 percent of patients whose treatment did not comply with the sepsis order set, 34 percent acquired one or more QVIs, with an average direct variable cost per case of $40,942. Meanwhile, of the 31 percent of patients whose treatment adhered to the core measure standard order set, 15 percent acquired one or more QVIs, with an average direct variable cost per case of $24,106. Thus, both the QVI rate and average direct variable cost per case for cases with one or more QVIs were lower for cases in which treatment followed the sepsis order set (p-values of < 0.0001 and 0.002, respectively).

The average direct variable cost per case for patients with a QVI, at $32,962, is significant compared with that without a QVI (i.e., $6,355). The data show that for patients with QVIs, on average, the length of stay (LOS) and cost per case were four to five times greater than for patients without QVIs.

Conclusion

By showing a significant difference in quality outcomes and costs between patients who were treated under standard care protocols and patients who were not treated under the protocols, this study's findings suggest there is value to be gained from continued usage and development of these standard order sets. The data suggest there is validity in long-held belief that standardizing processes improves outcomes for the patient and the hospital.

The findings also underscore the potential value of applying the lean methodology in a hospital setting. Standard order sets provide easy system navigation for physicians, resulting in less waste of physician's time, better outcomes for patients, and reduced direct care costs for the hospital.

The data also suggest that hospitals have ample opportunity to use lean methods to develop and increase the adoption of standard order sets. In the case study described here, standard order sets were only used 30 percent of the time, presenting a significant opportunity for improvement. Senior executives should review the usage rates of standard order sets in their own organizations and seek to understand what types of barriers might exist that keep physicians from using these clinical tools. Key questions these executives ask include the following:

- Are the order sets up to date?

- Are the order sets easy to find and/or use in the electronic health record?

- Are physicians and residents aware that the order sets exist?

The study's findings reinforce the view that promoting the usage of standard order sets constitutes a straightforward improvement initiative that correlates to lower costs and better patient outcomes.

As APMs become more prevalent, it will be incumbent on senior executives to be cognizant of all the various means available to their organizations for managing costs and reducing patient complications. Reducing complications by using standard care protocols, for example, allows hospitals to better manage patients after discharge and keep the cost of follow-up care low.

Data related to the cost of an episode of care are still in the early stages of being studied. Although such data continues to be developed and shared, hospitals executives should continue to look internally at how to reduce costs related to the initial anchor stay. Promoting the use of lean principles to develop standard care protocols and order sets and foster their widespread acceptance and use may be one of the most promising and effective places to start, with potential benefits in the form of both reduced costs and improved quality.

Republished, with permission, from the HFMA Early Edition Newsletter, November 4, 2016.
Three Westbrook Corporate Center, Suite 600, Westchester, IL 60154-5732.
For more information, call 800-252-HFMA or vist hfma.org

Epilogue

Looking Ahead

By Dan Michelson

The challenge of significantly bending the cost curve in healthcare is monumental and it can't be done in isolation. The silver lining of a healthcare's collective value-based future is the recognition that margin and mission can't be achieved independently.

The goal of *Margin + Mission: A Prescription for Solving Healthcare's Cost Crisis* is to help turn confusion into conversation and conversation into action by sharing ideas and examples. These examples provide a snapshot of our collective future.

A future where financial stewardship is central and clinical and fiscal responsibility go hand in hand.

A future where the value is a clear, defined and data-driven equation of outcomes over cost.

It's the future that Sister Irene forecasted and hoped for many years ago when she said "no margin, no mission."

Now it's our turn and our time to deliver on that vision of margin and mission.

It's a great responsibility.

It's a great opportunity.

It's time to get started.

About the Authors

Dan Michelson

Dan is the CEO of Strata Decision Technology where his focus is to ensure the company delivers on its mission to help heal healthcare. The Company's financial planning, analytics and performance platform is used by over 1,000 healthcare organizations, including many of the largest and most influential healthcare systems in the U.S. The company has been recognized multiple times as one of the fastest growing companies in the nation by *Inc. Magazine* and as one of the best places to work in healthcare by *Becker's Healthcare* and has received the prestigious "Best in KLAS" recognition for the highest customer satisfaction by KLAS Enterprises four times. Additionally, Dan is a two-time finalist for Illinois Technology CEO of the Year. With over 25 years of healthcare experience, Dan has been one of the industry's key thought leaders in developing the Decision Support, Financial Planning, Electronic Prescribing and Electronic Health Record markets, including serving on the Certification Commission for Healthcare Information Technology and authoring the books The *Electronic Physician* and *Margin + Mission: A Prescription for Curing Healthcare's Cost Crisis*. Prior to joining Strata, Dan spent 12 years as part of the leadership team that grew a healthcare software company from 100 to over 6,000 employees. He has provided strategy and process redesign consulting for many of the leading hospitals and health systems in the U.S. and served in leadership roles for Baxter Healthcare and AstraZeneca, two leading medical companies. Dan is the co-founder of projectMUSIC™, a benefit concert that sends underprivileged children to overnight camp and of HackHunger™, a collaborative of tech companies working to crack the code on childhood hunger. Dan earned his BS in Finance from Indiana University and his MBA from DePaul University. He is an avid runner, having completed 15 marathons. Dan lives in the Chicago area with his wife, Kim, and their two children, Emma and Ian.

Liz Kirk

Liz is the Senior Vice President of Client Services and Cost Improvement Solutions of Strata Decision Technology. With more than 15 years of experience working with healthcare providers, both as a hospital administrator and a consultant, Liz's role includes leadership of Strata's client services team, as well as the development and delivery of Strata's innovative application for continuous cost improvement. Prior to joining Strata, Liz was responsible for cost reduction and revenue improvement at Northwestern Memorial Hospital in Chicago, IL. She was also instrumental in developing revenue cycle consulting and technology services at Accretive Health and in starting the Revenue Cycle and Financial Improvement practice at GE Healthcare Performance Solutions. She began her career at Deloitte Consulting working with both payers and providers. Liz is certified Lean Six Sigma Black Belt, a Master Change Agent and the co-author of *Margin + Mission: A Prescription for Curing Healthcare's Cost Crisis*. She earned a MBA and MHA at the University of Minnesota and a BS in Finance at Trinity University in San Antonio, Texas. Liz lives in Chicago with her husband, Brian, and her daughter, Dylan.

Contributing Writers

Helen Adamopoulos: Freelance writer

Steve Allegretto: Vice President of Strategic Analysis and Financial Planning at Yale-New Haven Health System

Elizabeth Barker: Freelance writer and Senior Specialist, Digital Marketing at Alzheimer's Association

Jami Eddington: Solution Lead at Pareto Intelligence

Ayla Ellison: Reporter, *Becker's Hospital Review*

Laura Ramos Hegwer: Freelance writer

Alina Henderson: Director of Professional Services at Strata Decision Technology

Bob Herman: Reporter, *Modern Healthcare*

Jennifer Ittner: Director of Continuous Improvement at Strata Decision Technology

John Kenagy, PhD: Senior Vice President and Chief Information Officer at Legacy Health

Rene Letourneau: Freelance writer

Tushar Pandey: Vice President of Decision Support at Strata Decision Technology

Ben Shah: Chief Executive Officer at Olympia Orthopaedic Associates

Karen Wagner: Freelance writer

Acknowledgements

Thank you to the entire team at Strata Decision Technology who come to work every day with a passion to help heal healthcare by working with our customers to drive margin to fuel their mission. A special thank you to our long-term employees for their ongoing dedication and commitment: Peter Azra, Chris Barth, Josh Bautista, Cara Boaz, Rachael Britnell, Becky Caden, Andy Cerny, Leon Corbeille, Michael Edwards, Graydon Foreman, Joel Gerber, Josh Goodman, Hari Gutta, Lynette Jasuta, Srujana Kandimalla, Angela Kirkwood, Mady Koch, Divya Kondaveeti, Adam Kowalski, Mitch Leitch, Nathan Leroy, Deb Magsam, Lindley Mahinay, Aditya Malhotra, Laura Marchese, Christie Markiewicz, Shikha Mehra, Melissa Memmolo, David Moldawer, Jo Moore, Hung Nguyen, Tushar Pandey, Brian Parrott, Tushar Patel, Matthew Price, Ryan Reimer, Debra Reitz, Scott Schoenknecht, Emaad Shehzad, Joe Siegle, Michael Slovenkay, Jaclyn Spitz, Stan Stafford, Samantha Stark, Frank Stevens, Katie Stull, Hansel Tan, Elizabeth Tandy, Jeff Teske, Kris Wanintradul and Dan Van De Voorde. An additional thank you to Rachael Britnell, Rachel Broghammer, Andy Cerny, Brian Groves, Tyler Entingh, Heidi Farrell, Neil Hunn, Lynette Jasuta, Martin Luethi and John Martino for their contributions to the Strata story.

Most importantly, we would like to thank the 1,000 hospitals and 200 healthcare delivery systems who we are lucky enough to call our customers, our partners and our friends. We are honored to serve them in support of their mission. Representing our customer base in this book are the following organizations: Augusta University Health System, Baptist Health Arkansas, Children's Healthcare of Atlanta, Fairview Health Services, Johns Hopkins Bloomberg School of Public Health, Legacy Health, Mission Health System, Parrish Medical Center, ProMedica, Spectrum Healthcare, University of Virginia Medical Center, Wake Forest Baptist Medical Center and Yale-New Haven Health System.